Edexcel

higher

GCSE Modular Mathematics

unit 2

Keith Pledger

Gareth Cole

Peter Jolly

Graham Newman

Joe Petran

www.heinemann.co.uk

✓ Free online support
✓ Useful weblinks
✓ 24 hour online ordering

01865 888058

Heinemann
Inspiring generations

Heinemann is an imprint of Pearson Education Limited,
a company incorporated in England and Wales, having its
registered office at Edinburgh Gate, Harlow, Essex, CM20 2JE.
Registered company number: 872828

Heinemann is a registered trademark of Pearson Education Limited

© Pearson Education Ltd, 2006

First published 2006

10 09 08 07
10 9 8 7 6 5 4 3 2 1

British Library Cataloguing in Publication Data is available from the British Library on
request.

ISBN: 978 0 435585 31 0

Typeset by Tech-Set Ltd, Gateshead, Tyne and Wear
Original illustrations © Pearson Education Limited, 2006
Cover design by mccdesign
Printed and bound at Scotprint
Cover photo: Digital Vision

Acknowledgements

This high quality material is endorsed by Edexcel and has been through a rigorous quality
assurance programme to ensure that it is a suitable companion to the specification for
both learners and teachers. This does not mean that its contents will be used verbatim
when setting examinations nor is it to be read as being the official specification – a copy
of which is available at www.edexcel.org.uk.

The publisher's and authors' thanks are due to Edexcel Limited for permission to
reproduce questions from past examination papers. These are marked with an [E]. The
answers have been provided by the authors and are not the responsibility of Edexcel
Limited.

The authors and publisher would like to thank the following individuals and organization
for permission to reproduce photographs: Corbis pp3, 25, 41, 91, 116, 130; MorgueFile/
Kenn Kiser p13; MorgueFile/Clara Natoli p18; Getty Images/PhotoDisc pp19, 32, 33;
MorgueFile/Mary Thorman p21; Photos.com pp28, 29, 44 bottom; MorgueFile/Phaedra
Wilkinson p35; Pearson Education Ltd/Gareth Boden p42; Pearson Education Ltd/
Malcolm Harris p44 top; MorgueFile/Scott Liddell p87; Dreamstime.com/Michael
Osterrieder p88; Empics p113; iStockPhoto/Andy Platt p114; Dreamstime.com/Kendy
Kaveney p119; Dreamstime.com/Feng Yu p123

Every effort has been made to contact copyright holders of material reproduced in this
book. Any omissions will be rectified in subsequent printings if notice is given to the
publishers.

Publishing team

Editorial	Katherine Pate, James Orr, Evan Curnow, Lyn Imeson, Elizabeth Bowden, Lindsey Besley
Design	Christopher Howson
Production	Helen McCreath
Picture Research	Chrissie Martin

Tel: 01865 888058   www.heinemann.co.uk

Quick reference to chapters

Contents

■ = New stage 1
■ = New stage 2

3 Index notation and standard form

10 Perimeter, area and volume

Practice questions

About this book

This book has been carefully matched to the new two-tier modular specification for Edexcel GCSE Maths. It covers everything you need to know to achieve success in Unit 2. The author team is made up of the Chief Examiner, the Chair of Examiners, Principal Examiners and Senior Moderators, all experienced teachers with an excellent understanding of the Edexcel specification.

Key features

Chapters are divided into **sections**. In each section you will find:

- **key points**, highlighted throughout like this

> - When adding and subtracting decimals make sure you write the digits in their correct place value columns.

- **examples** that show you how to tackle questions
- an **exercise** to help develop your understanding.

Each chapter ends with a **mixed exercise** and a **summary of key points**. Mixed exercises, which include past exam questions marked with an [E], are designed to test your understanding across the chapter.

Hint boxes are used to make explanations clearer. They may also remind you of previously learned facts or tell you where in the book to find more information.

> Ordering from largest to smallest is writing in **descending order**.

An **examination practice paper** is included to help you prepare for the exam at the end of the unit.

Answers are provided at the back of the book to use as your teacher directs.

Quick reference and detailed Contents pages

Use the thumb spots on the **Quick reference page** to turn to the right chapter quickly.

Use the detailed **Contents** to help you find a section on a particular topic. The summary and reference codes on the right show your teacher the part(s) of the specification covered by each section of the book. (For example, NA2a refers to Number and algebra, section 2 Numbers and the Number system, subsection a.)

Teaching and learning software

References to the *Heinemann* Edexcel GCSE Mathematics **Teaching and learning software** are included for you and your teacher. (The number refers to the relevant chapter from the linear course on which the software is based.)

> **8** Calculating with fractions

Use of a calculator

 These symbols show where you must, or must not, use a calculator.

1 Integers and powers

1.1 Integers and place value

- An **integer** is any positive or negative whole number. Zero is also an integer.
- The value of a digit in a number depends on its position in the number. This is its **place value**.

Example 1

(a) Which of the following numbers are integers?

$$30, 0.3, -3, 0, -3.3$$

(b) Write them in order of size, largest first.

(a) 30, -3 and 0 are integers.

(b) 30, 0.3, 0, -3, -3.3

> 0.3 and -3.3 are not whole numbers.

Example 2

(a) Write 2 467 381 in words.

(b) Write five hundred and forty thousand, two hundred and sixteen in figures.

(a) Two million, four hundred and sixty-seven thousand, three hundred and eighty-one

(b) 540 216

> 2 467 381 is
>
> | millions | thousands | hundreds | tens | units |
> |----------|-----------|----------|------|-------|
> | 2 | 467 | 3 | 8 | 1 |

Exercise 1A

1 From each list of numbers write down the integers in order of size, starting with the largest.

(a) 6.3, 63, -6.3, -63, 0

(b) 562, 5.62, -5620, -0.562

(c) 1 million, 0.01, -2, 30 000, -2.3

2 Write these numbers in words.

(a) 432 (b) 8200 (c) 6370 (d) 16 892

(e) 372 859 (f) 483 002 (g) 3 215 468 (h) 3 000 682

3   Write these numbers in digits.

(a)   four hundred and sixty-three

(b)   fifteen thousand and twenty-seven

(c)   one hundred and sixteen thousand, two hundred and twenty-five

(d)   three hundred and five thousand, one hundred and one

(e)   two million, three hundred and twenty-seven thousand and thirty-five

(f)   half a million

1.2 Calculating with negative numbers

- You can use negative numbers to describe quantities such as temperatures less than 0 °C.
- Subtracting a positive number is the same as adding the negative number.
- Subtracting a negative number is the same as adding the positive number.
- Adding a negative number is the same as subtracting the positive number.
- This table shows the signs you get when you multiply or divide two numbers.

+	×/÷	+	=	+
+	×/÷	−	=	−
−	×/÷	+	=	−
−	×/÷	−	=	+

Negative number × positive number → negative answer.

Example 3

Work out

(a) $2 - +3$

(b) $-3 - -2$

(c) $4 + -2$

(d) $-3 + +1$

(a) $2 - +3 = -1$

$2 - +3$ is the same as $2 + -3$.
Start at 2 and go down 3 to get to −1.

(b) $-3 - -2 = -1$

> $-3 - -2$ is the same as $-3 + +2$.
> Start at -3 and go up 2 to get to -1.

(c) $4 + -2 = 2$

> $4 + -2$ is the same as $4 - 2$.
> Start at 4 and go down 2 to get to $+2$.

(d) $-3 + +1 = -2$

> $-3 + +1$.
> Start at -3 and go up 1 to get to -2.

Example 4

Work out
(a) 15×-3 (b) $-8 \div -2$
(c) -16×-3 (d) $-10 \div 5$

+	×/÷	+	=	+
+	×/÷	−	=	−
−	×/÷	+	=	−
−	×/÷	−	=	+

(a) $15 \times -3 = -45$ (b) $-8 \div -2 = +4$
(c) $-16 \times -3 = +48$ (d) $-10 \div 5 = -2$

Exercise 1B

1 Work out
(a) $-4 + -3$ (b) $9 - +5$ (c) $8 - -2$ (d) $5 + +4$
(e) $-7 - -6$ (f) $-2 + +4$ (g) $6 + -8$ (h) $-3 - +7$

2 Work out
(a) -3×-8 (b) -5×3 (c) $24 \div -3$ (d) $-36 \div -12$
(e) -8×5 (f) $-48 \div 8$ (g) 6×-5 (h) $-50 \div -5$

3 A diver dives to a depth of -27 metres. A second diver dives to a depth of -16 metres. What is the difference in the depths of the dives?

4 The temperature at the Arctic Circle is recorded as $-18\ ^\circ\text{C}$ one night. The following day it rises by $6\ ^\circ\text{C}$. What is the temperature during the day?

5 Copy and complete the following tables.

(a)

×	-2	6	-7
5		30	
-3			
8	-16		

(2nd number)

(b)

−	2	-3	8
-4			
5		-8	
-1			

(2nd number)

(c)

+	-3	-4	2
5	2		
1			
-6			

(2nd number)

(d)

÷	16	-24	-36
-2		12	
4			
-8			

(2nd number)

1.3 Rounding to one significant figure

- The first significant figure is the first non-zero digit in a number, counting from the left.
- To write a number to one significant figure (1 s.f.), look at the place value of the first significant figure and round to this place value.
- To estimate the answer to a calculation, round all numbers to one significant figure and do the simpler calculation.

Example 5

Estimate the answer to $\dfrac{563 \times 2140}{25}$

563 to 1 s.f. = 600   2140 to 1 s.f. = 2000   25 to 1 s.f. = 30

First round all the numbers to one significant figure.

This digit is greater than 5 so round up.

This digit is less than 5 so round down.

This digit is 5 so round up.

An estimate is $\dfrac{600 \times 2000}{30} = 40\,000$

Example 6

Estimate the answers to these questions by rounding all the numbers to 1 s.f.

(a) 17.8×4.2 (b) $234 \div 13.2$ (c) $\dfrac{5.8 \times 7.4}{3.4 + 6.9}$

(a) 17.8×4.2 becomes $20 \times 4 = 80$ as an estimate.

(b) $234 \div 13.2$ becomes $200 \div 10 = 20$ as an estimate.

(c) $\dfrac{5.8 \times 7.4}{3.4 + 6.9}$ becomes $\dfrac{6 \times 7}{3 + 7} = \dfrac{42}{10} = 4.2$ as an estimate.

Exercise 1C

1 Write these numbers to 1 significant figure.

(a) 36　　　　(b) 237　　　　(c) 5584　　　　(d) 3.21

(e) 16.8　　　(f) 8500　　　(g) 2159　　　(h) 3841

2 For each of the following calculations

(i) write down a calculation that can be used to estimate the answer

(ii) work out an estimated answer.

(a) 37 × 42　　　　(b) 83 ÷ 18　　　　(c) 237 ÷ 39

(d) 457 × 28　　　(e) $\dfrac{876 \times 15}{12}$　　　(f) $\dfrac{29 \times 23}{11 \times 27}$

3 43 238 spectators watched a pop concert. They paid £18 for a ticket. Estimate the total income from the ticket sales.

4 There are 1.76 pints in 1 litre. Estimate how many pints there are in 19 litres.

1.4 Rounding to a number of significant figures

- You can round numbers to a given number of significant figures (s.f.).

Example 7

Round 746.501 to (a) 1 s.f. (b) 2 s.f. (c) 3 s.f. (d) 4 s.f. (e) 5 s.f.

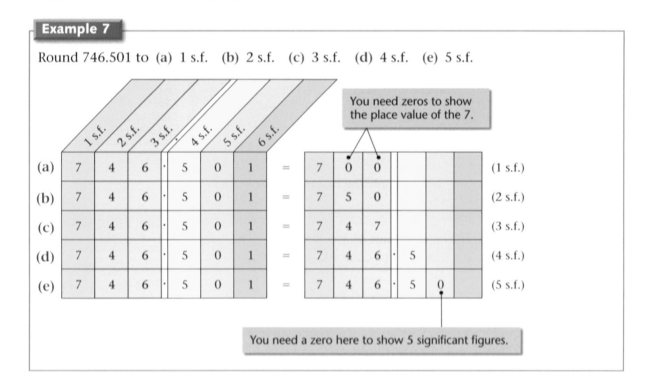

You need zeros to show the place value of the 7.

You need a zero here to show 5 significant figures.

Exercise 1D

1 Round these numbers to 2 s.f.

    (a) 45.6   (b) 437   (c) 3.682

    (d) 5472.3   (e) 0.002 35   (f) 0.095

> In 0.002 35 the first significant figure is 2.

2 Round these numbers to 3 s.f.

    (a) 945.3   (b) 10 678   (c) 789 421

    (d) 0.834 52   (e) 0.002 378 1   (f) 0.048 04

3 Round these numbers to the number of significant figures given in the brackets.

    (a) 4892   (2 s.f.) (b) 78 348 (1 s.f.)   (c) 378.42 (2 s.f.)

    (d) 0.028 94 (3 s.f.) (e) 2.603 (3 s.f.)   (f) 4999 (3 s.f.)

4 Work out an estimate for

    (a) 72×39 (b) $123 \div 19.4$ (c) 6.35×2.96

    (d) $7.8 \div 1.89$ (e) $\dfrac{23.9 \times 96}{49.6}$ (f) $(986 \times 237) + 407$

    (g) $\dfrac{0.28 \times 0.59}{1.01}$ (h) 3.14×4.5^2

> Round each number to 1 s.f.

1.5 Squares, square roots, cubes and cube roots

- You need to memorise all the square numbers from 2^2 to 15^2 and the corresponding square roots.
- If $x \times x = A$, then x is the **square root** of A, written $\sqrt{A}$.
  For example, $4 \times 4 = 16$, so 4 is the square root of 16, written $\sqrt{16} = 4$

> Notice that $-4 \times -4 = 16$, so -4 is also a square root of 16.
> $\sqrt{16} = \pm 4$

- You need to memorise the cubes of 2, 3, 4, 5 and 10 and the corresponding cube roots.
- To find the cube of any number, multiply the number by itself, then multiply by the number again.
  For example $7^3 = 7 \times 7 \times 7 = 343$

> $-2 \times -2 \times -2 = -8$
> So $\sqrt[3]{8} = -2$

- If $y \times y \times y = A$, then y is the **cube root** of A, written $\sqrt[3]{A}$.
  For example, $2 \times 2 \times 2 = 8$, so 2 is the cube root of 8, written $\sqrt[3]{8} = 2$.

> For example $\sqrt{18} = 4.2426406... = 4.24$ (2 d.p.)

- You can use the square root function key on a calculator to find the square root of a positive number.

- You can use the cube root function key on a calculator to find the cube root of any positive or negative number.

> For example $\sqrt[3]{18} = 2.6207413... = 2.62$ (2 d. p.)

Exercise 1E

1 Write down from memory

(a) 3^2	(b) 4^3	(c) 7^2	(d) 8^2
(e) 10^2	(f) 2^2	(g) 6^2	(h) 3^3
(i) 10^3	(j) 4^2	(k) 5^3	(l) 12^2
(m) 13^2	(n) 2^3	(o) 5^2	(p) 9^2
(q) 11^2	(r) 14^2	(s) 15^2	

2 Write down from memory

(a) $\sqrt{64}$	(b) $\sqrt{9}$	(c) $\sqrt{25}$	(d) $\sqrt{144}$
(e) $\sqrt{169}$	(f) $\sqrt{225}$	(g) $\sqrt{4}$	(h) $\sqrt{100}$
(i) $\sqrt{36}$	(j) $\sqrt{121}$	(k) $\sqrt{49}$	(l) $\sqrt{81}$
(m) $\sqrt{16}$	(n) $\sqrt{196}$	(o) $\sqrt[3]{8}$	(p) $\sqrt[3]{125}$
(q) $\sqrt[3]{27}$	(r) $\sqrt[3]{64}$	(s) $\sqrt[3]{1000}$	

3 Estimate, to the nearest whole number, the value of

(a) $\sqrt{50}$ (b) $\sqrt{38}$ (c) $\sqrt{128}$

(d) $\sqrt{69}$ (e) $\sqrt{24}$

4 Use your calculator to work out

(a) $\sqrt{77}$	(b) $\sqrt[3]{96}$	(c) $\sqrt[3]{-8.2}$
(d) $(-1.3)^3$	(e) 62.3^2	(f) $\sqrt{523}$
(g) $(-71.7)^2$	(h) $\sqrt[3]{-14.5}$	(i) $\sqrt{26\,900}$

Give your answers to 3 significant figures.

1.6 Index notation

- The ^{2} in 7^2 is called an **index** or a **power**. It tells you how many times the **base number** (7, here) must be multiplied by itself.

Example 8

Rewrite these expressions using index notation.

(a) $3 \times 3 \times 3$ (b) $4 \times 4 \times 3 \times 3 \times 3$

(c) $2 \times 2 \times 2 \times 2 \times 2$ (d) 3

(a) 3^3 (b) $4^2 \times 3^3$ (c) 2^5 (d) 3^1

Example 9

Evaluate

(a) 4^3 (b) $2^3 \times 3^2$ (c) 5^4

(a) $4^3 = 4 \times 4 \times 4$ (b) $2^3 \times 3^2 = 2 \times 2 \times 2 \times 3 \times 3$
$\qquad = 64$ $\qquad\qquad\qquad = 8 \times 9$
$\qquad\qquad\qquad\qquad\qquad = 72$

(c) $5^4 = 5 \times 5 \times 5 \times 5$
$\qquad = 625$

Example 10

Find the value of x when
(a) $6^x = 36$ (b) $2^x = 32$ (c) $4^x = 256$

(a) $6 \times 6 = 36$ so $6^2 = 36$ and $x = 2$.
(b) $2 \times 2 \times 2 \times 2 \times 2 = 32$ so $2^5 = 32$ and $x = 5$.
(c) $4 \times 4 \times 4 \times 4 = 256$ so $4^4 = 256$ and $x = 4$.

Exercise 1F

1 Rewrite these expressions using index notation.
(a) $5 \times 5 \times 5 \times 5$ (b) $2 \times 2 \times 2 \times 2 \times 2$
(c) $6 \times 6 \times 6$ (d) $7 \times 7 \times 7 \times 2 \times 2$
(e) $3 \times 3 \times 8 \times 8 \times 8 \times 8$ (f) $4 \times 4 \times 4 \times 4 \times 2 \times 2 \times 2$
(g) $2 \times 2 \times 2 \times 3 \times 3 \times 4 \times 4 \times 4$

2 Evaluate
(a) 2^4 (b) 3^5 (c) 6^3 (d) 7^4
(e) 8^3 (f) $2^4 \times 9^3$ (g) $2^6 \times 4^5$ (h) $5^3 \times 3^4$
(i) $2^7 \times 3^5$ (j) $3^3 \times 4^1$

3 Find x when
(a) $5^x = 125$ (b) $3^x = 81$ (c) $2^x = 64$ (d) $10^x = 10\,000$
(e) $9^x = 81$ (f) $3^x = 27$ (g) $2^x = 16$ (h) $7^x = 1$

1.7 Index laws

- To multiply powers of the same number, add the indices.
  In general: $x^n \times x^m = x^{n+m}$

- To divide powers of the same number, subtract the indices.
  In general: $x^n \div x^m = x^{n-m}$

'Indices' is the plural of 'index'.

Example 11

Simplify
(a) $3^2 \times 3^4$ (b) $4^3 \times 4^5$ (c) $2^5 \div 2^3$
(d) $10^4 \div 10^2$ (e) $\dfrac{2^6 \times 2^3}{2^4}$ (f) $x^3 \times x^2$

(a) $3^2 \times 3^4 = 3^{2+4} = 3^6$ (b) $4^3 \times 4^5 = 4^{3+5} = 4^8$
(c) $2^5 \div 2^3 = 2^{5-3} = 2^2$ (d) $10^4 \div 10^2 = 10^{4-2} = 10^2$
(e) $\dfrac{2^6 \times 2^3}{2^4} = \dfrac{2^{6+3}}{2^4} = \dfrac{2^9}{2^4} = 2^{9-4} = 2^5$ (f) $x^3 \times x^2 = x^{3+2} = x^5$

Exercise 1G

Simplify

1 $8^2 \times 8^4$ **2** $3^4 \times 3^2$ **3** $2^6 \times 2^3$

4 5×5^2 **5** $3^4 \div 3^2$ **6** $7^4 \div 7^2$

7 $8^5 \div 8^3$ **8** $10^4 \div 10$ **9** $8^2 \times 8^3 \times 8^4$

10 $2^3 \times 2^5 \times 2$ **11** $4^3 \times 4 \times 4^2$ **12** $\dfrac{6^3 \times 6^2}{6^3}$

13 $\dfrac{2^5 \div 2^2}{2^4}$ **14** $\dfrac{4^8 \times 4^4}{4^2}$ **15** $\dfrac{9^4 \div 9^2}{9}$

16 $\dfrac{10^6 \div 10^2}{10^4}$ **17** $x^4 \times x^3$ **18** $y^4 \div y^2$

19 $\dfrac{a^2 \times a^4}{a^3}$ **20** $\dfrac{z^4 \div z}{z^2}$

1.8 BIDMAS

- BIDMAS is a made-up word to help you remember the order of operations.

$$B \; I \; D \; M \; A \; S$$

Brackets   Indices   Divide   Multiply   Add   Subtract
             (powers
             and roots)

- When operations are the same, do them in the order they appear.

Example 12

Work out

(a) $6 + 3 \times 4$ (b) $\dfrac{48 - 16}{4^2}$ (c) $(2^2 + 3^2) \div 2$

(a) $6 + 3 \times 4$
$= 6 + 12$
$= 18$

(b) $\dfrac{48 - 16}{4^2}$ This line acts as a bracket.
$= (48 - 16) \div 4^2$
$= 32 \div 4^2$
$= 32 \div 16$
$= 2$

(c) $(2^2 + 3^2) \div 2$
$= ((2 \times 2) + (3 \times 3)) \div 2$
$= (4 \quad + \quad 9) \div 2$
$= \quad\quad 13 \div 2$
$= 6.5$

Exercise 1H

1 Work out

   (a) $5 + 4 \times 7$

   (b) $8 - 8 \div 2$

   (c) $(6 + 2) \times 3$

   (d) $(5 + 3) \times (6 - 4)$

   (e) $\dfrac{9 \times 3}{5 \times 2}$

   (f) $(2 + 7)^2$

   (g) $\sqrt{(5 + 4)}$

   (h) $3^2 + 7$

   (i) $\dfrac{\sqrt{(5 + 20)}}{3 + 2}$

   (j) $\dfrac{6^2}{\sqrt{9} \times 2}$

   (k) $(5 + 4)^2 - (3 - 5)^2$

   (l) $8 + 2^2 \times 3 \div (10 - 6)$

2 Make these expressions correct by replacing the * with $+$, $-$, $\times$ or $\div$. Use brackets if you need to.

   (a) $3 * 4 * 5 = 27$

   (b) $2 * 3 * 2 * 3 = 25$

   (c) $6 * 7 * 8 * 9 = 1$

   (d) $10 * 9 * 8 * 7 = 34$

   (e) $3 * 3 * 3 = 0$

   (f) $3 * 3 * 3 = 2$

1.9 Reciprocals

- The reciprocal of n is $1 \div n$ or $\dfrac{1}{n}$.
- Multiplying a number by its reciprocal gives 1.
- Zero has no reciprocal because you cannot divide by zero.

Example 13

Find the reciprocal of

(a) 6   (b) 0.2   (c) $\frac{2}{5}$

(a) $1 \div 6 = \dfrac{1}{6}$

(b) $1 \div 0.2 = 5$

Check:
reciprocal of $6 \times 6 = 1$
$\dfrac{1}{6} \times 6 = 1$ ✓

Check: $5 \times 0.2 = 1$ ✓

(c) $1 \div \dfrac{2}{5} = 1 \times \dfrac{5}{2} = \dfrac{5}{2}$

$= 2\dfrac{1}{2}$

Check: $\dfrac{\overset{1}{2}}{\underset{1}{5}} \times \dfrac{\overset{1}{5}}{\underset{1}{2}} = 1$ ✓

Exercise 1I

1 Find the reciprocal of

   (a) 4

   (b) 3

   (c) 2

   (d) 7

   (e) 9

   (f) 20

2 Find the reciprocal of

    (a) 0.1   (b) 0.5   (c) 0.25   (d) 0.4   (e) 0.3   (f) 0.125

3 Find the reciprocal, in its simplest form, of

    (a) $\frac{3}{5}$ (b) $\frac{2}{7}$ (c) $\frac{1}{4}$ (d) $\frac{1}{8}$ (e) $\frac{3}{16}$ (f) $\frac{5}{8}$

4 Find the reciprocal of

    (a) x (b) y (c) $\frac{1}{x}$ (d) y^3

1.10 LCM, HCF and prime factor decomposition

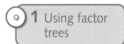

1 Using factor trees

- A **factor** of a number is a whole number that divides exactly into it. The factors of a number include 1 and the number itself.
- **Multiples** of a number are the results of multiplying the number by the positive whole numbers.
- A **prime number** is a whole number greater than 1 that only has two factors: itself and 1.
- A number written as a product of prime numbers is written in **prime factor form**.
- The **highest common factor** (HCF) of two numbers is the highest factor common to both of them.
- The **lowest common multiple** (LCM) of two numbers is the lowest multiple common to both of them.

Example 14

(a) Write 36 in prime factor form.

(b) Find the highest common factor (HCF) of 36 and 12.

(c) Find the lowest common multiple (LCM) of 3 and 4.

Method 1

(a) $36 = 2 \times 18$
      $= 2 \times 2 \times 9$
      $= 2 \times 2 \times 3 \times 3$

    which can be simplified to $2^2 \times 3^2$.

(b) $36 = ②\times②\times③\times 3$
    $24 = ②\times②\times 2 \times ③$
    HCF of 24 and 36 is $2 \times 2 \times 3 = 12$.

(c) 3:   3,   6,   9,   ⑫,   15
    4:   4,   8,   ⑫,   16
    LCM of 3 and 4 is 12.

Method 2

36
  / \
②   18
    / \
   ② 9
     / \
   ③ ③

Using a factor tree.

Write each number in prime factor form.

Pick out the factors common to both numbers.

Write a list of multiples for each number.

The LCM is the lowest number that appears in both lists.

Exercise 1J

1 Write down all the factors of
   (a) 48   (b) 360   (c) 29
   (d) 100   (e) 71   (f) 645

2 Write down the numbers in question **1** that are prime numbers.

3 Write down the first five multiples of
   (a) 4   (b) 7   (c) 11   (d) 20

4 Write these numbers in prime factor form, using index notation.
   (a) 50   (b) 72   (c) 450   (d) 840

5 Find the HCF of
   (a) 9 and 15   (b) 4 and 14   (c) 12 and 20
   (d) 6, 15 and 21   (e) 8, 24 and 36

6 Find the LCM of
   (a) 6 and 8   (b) 5 and 7   (c) 4 and 6
   (d) 2, 3 and 4   (e) 5, 6 and 10

7 Given that $a = 2^3 \times 3 \times 5^2$ and $b = 2 \times 3^3 \times 7$ write down
   (a) the LCM of a and b
   (b) the HCF of a and b.

Mixed exercise 1

1 A list of numbers is written below.
       256 214
       0
       three hundred and two thousand four hundred and twelve
       $-73\,864$
   From the list
   (a) write down the integers
   (b) write down the first number in words
   (c) write the fourth number in figures.

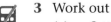

2 Work out
   (a) $-6 + -3$ (b) $7 - -3$ (c) $8 - +4$ (d) $-3 + +5$

3 Work out
   (a) -8×2 (b) $-10 \div -5$ (c) $6 \div -3$ (d) -7×-5

4 For each of the following calculations

    (i) write down a calculation that could be used to estimate the answer

    (ii) write down the estimated answer.

    (a) $\dfrac{281 \times 18}{497}$ (b) $\dfrac{2.4 \times 7.9}{1.8^2}$ (c) $\dfrac{8130 \div 381}{\sqrt[3]{7.6}}$

 5 Estimate the cost of 27 books at £19.95 each.

6 Round each number to the number of significant figures given in the brackets.

    (a) 37.2   (2 s.f.)   (b) 473   (1 s.f.)

    (c) 0.007 52 (2 s.f.)   (d) 96 345 (3 s.f.)

    (e) 489.302 (5 s.f.)

7 Write down from memory

    (a) 4^2 (b) 12^2 (c) 8^2 (d) 13^2 (e) $\sqrt{49}$

    (f) $\sqrt{196}$ (g) $\sqrt{225}$ (h) 4^3 (i) 5^3 (j) $\sqrt[3]{8}$

8 Rewrite these expressions using index notation.

    (a) $5 \times 5 \times 5$ (b) $4 \times 4 \times 4 \times 4$

    (c) $2 \times 2 \times 3 \times 3 \times 3$ (d) $5 \times 5 \times 7 \times 7$

9 Evaluate

    (a) 8^3 (b) 10^4 (c) 5^4

    (d) $2^4 \times 3^2$ (e) $5^2 \times 2^5$

10 Find x when

    (a) $9^x = 81$ (b) $2^x = 16$ (c) $10^x = 1000$

11 Here are some numbers.

    From the numbers in the cloud write down

    (a) the square numbers

    (b) the cube numbers

    (c) the prime numbers

    (d) factors of 27

    (e) multiples of 3.

 12 Simplify

    (a) $2^3 \times 2^4$ (b) $5^3 \times 5^2$ (c) $7^5 \div 7^2$

    (d) 3×3^4 (e) $9^8 \div 9^4$ (f) $8^3 \div 8$

    (g) $\dfrac{7^2 \times 7^4}{7^3}$ (h) $\dfrac{6^4 \div 6}{6^2}$ (i) $5^3 \times 5^6 \div 5^4$

13 Write down the value of
  (a) 2.5^2
  (b) the square of 10.1
  (c) 6.4 cubed
  (d) $\sqrt[3]{64.9}$
  (e) $\sqrt{38}$
  (f) 2.1^3
  (g) 6.3 squared
  (h) the cube of 2.4
  (i) the positive square root of 5.76
  (j) $\sqrt[3]{-8}$

14 Use BIDMAS to work out the value of
  (a) $(7 - 3) \times (5 + 3)$
  (b) $\dfrac{100}{4 \times 5}$
  (c) $(2 + 5)^2 \div (9 - 2)$
  (d) $5 + 3^2 \times 2 \div (3 - 9)$

15 Write in prime factor form
  (a) 180
  (b) 196
  (c) 600

16 Find the highest common factor (HCF) of
  (a) 12 and 18
  (b) 42 and 24
  (c) 6, 12 and 15

17 Find the lowest common multiple (LCM) of
  (a) 4 and 5
  (b) 6 and 8
  (c) 2, 6 and 8

18 Find the reciprocal of
  (a) 9
  (b) 6
  (c) 0.5
  (d) 0.625
  (e) $\dfrac{4}{5}$
  (f) $\dfrac{3}{7}$
  (g) x
  (h) $\dfrac{1}{y}$

Summary of key points

1 An **integer** is any positive or negative whole number. Zero is also an integer.

2 The value of a digit in a number depends on its position in the number. This is its **place value**.

3 You can use negative numbers to describe quantities such as temperatures less than 0 °C.

4 Subtracting a positive number is the same as adding the negative number.

5 Subtracting a negative number is the same as adding the positive number.

6 Adding a negative number is the same as subtracting the positive number.

7 This table shows the signs you get when you multiply or divide two numbers.

+	×/÷	+	=	+
+	×/÷	−	=	−
−	×/÷	+	=	−
−	×/÷	−	=	+

8 The first significant figure is the first non-zero digit in a number, counting from the left.

9 To write a number to one significant figure (1 s.f.), look at the place value of the first significant figure and round to this place value.

10 To estimate the answer to a calculation, round all numbers to one significant figure and do the simpler calculation.

11 You can round numbers to a given number of significant figures (s.f.).

12 You need to memorise all the square numbers from 2^2 to 15^2 and the corresponding square roots.

13 If $x \times x = A$, then x is the square root of A, written $\sqrt{A}$.

14 You need to memorise the cubes of 2, 3, 4, 5 and 10 and the corresponding cube roots.

15 To find the cube of any number, multiply the number by itself, then multiply by the number again. For example $7^3 = 7 \times 7 \times 7 = 343$

16 If $y \times y \times y = A$, then y is the **cube root** of A, written $\sqrt[3]{A}$. For example, $2 \times 2 \times 2 = 8$, so 2 is the cube root of 8, written $\sqrt[3]{8} = 2$.

17 You can use the square root function key on a calculator to find the square root of a positive number.

18 You can use the cube root function key on a calculator to find the cube root of any positive or negative number.

19 The ^{2} in 7^2 is called an **index** or a **power**. It tells you how many times the **base number** (7, here) must be multiplied by itself.

20 To multiply powers of the same number, add the indices. In general: $x^n \times x^m = x^{n+m}$

21 To divide powers of the same number, subtract the indices. In general: $x^n \div x^m = x^{n-m}$

22 BIDMAS is a made-up word to help you remember the order of operations.

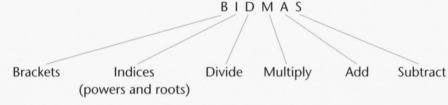

B I D M A S

Brackets   Indices   Divide   Multiply   Add   Subtract
(powers and roots)

23 When operations are the same, do them in the order they appear.

24 The reciprocal of n is $1 \div n$ or $\frac{1}{n}$.

25 Multiplying a number by its reciprocal gives 1.

26 Zero has no reciprocal because you cannot divide by zero.

27 A **factor** of a number is a whole number that divides exactly into it. The factors of a number include 1 and the number itself.

28 **Multiples** of a number are the results of multiplying the number by the positive whole numbers.

29 A **prime number** is a whole number greater than 1 that only has two factors: itself and 1.

30 A number written as a product of prime numbers is written in **prime factor form**.

31 The **highest common factor** (HCF) of two numbers is the highest factor common to both of them.

32 The **lowest common multiple** (LCM) of two numbers is the lowest multiple common to both of them.

2 Fractions, decimals and percentages

2.1 Improper fractions and mixed numbers

- In a fraction:

  This number shows how many parts you have.

  The top number is called the **numerator**.

  $$\frac{3}{4}$$

  This number shows the total number of parts there are.

  The bottom number is called the **denominator**.

- A fraction whose numerator is larger than its denominator is called an **improper fraction**. For example, $\frac{5}{2}$ is an improper fraction.

- An improper fraction can be written as a **mixed number**, with a whole number part and a fraction part. For example, $\frac{5}{2} = 2\frac{1}{2}$ as a mixed number.

- A mixed number can be written as an improper fraction.

Example 1

Write as an improper fraction

(a) $3\frac{1}{2}$

(b) $2\frac{1}{4}$

(a) 3 can be written as $\frac{6}{2}$.

  So $3\frac{1}{2} = \frac{6}{2} + \frac{1}{2} = \frac{7}{2}$

  > 3 = 6 halves = $\frac{6}{2}$

(b) 2 can be written as $\frac{8}{4}$.

  So $2\frac{1}{4} = \frac{8}{4} + \frac{1}{4} = \frac{9}{4}$

  > 2 = 8 quarters = $\frac{8}{4}$

Example 2

Change these improper fractions into mixed numbers.

(a) $\frac{23}{8}$

(b) $\frac{13}{5}$

(a) Arrange $\frac{23}{8}$ into as many groups of $\frac{8}{8}$ ($\frac{8}{8} = 1$) as possible.

  $\frac{23}{8} = \frac{8}{8} + \frac{8}{8} + \frac{7}{8} = 2\frac{7}{8}$

(b) $\frac{13}{5} = \frac{5}{5} + \frac{5}{5} + \frac{3}{5} = 2\frac{3}{5}$

Exercise 2A

1 Write these mixed numbers as improper fractions.

(a) $1\frac{1}{2}$ (b) $1\frac{1}{4}$ (c) $1\frac{2}{5}$ (d) $2\frac{1}{3}$ (e) $3\frac{3}{4}$

(f) $4\frac{3}{5}$ (g) $6\frac{5}{9}$ (h) $8\frac{3}{10}$ (i) $10\frac{7}{8}$ (j) $10\frac{5}{28}$

2 Write these improper fractions as mixed numbers.

(a) $\frac{7}{2}$ (b) $\frac{9}{4}$ (c) $\frac{17}{8}$ (d) $\frac{16}{5}$ (e) $\frac{13}{2}$

(f) $\frac{23}{10}$ (g) $\frac{23}{5}$ (h) $\frac{32}{6}$ (i) $\frac{42}{20}$ (j) $\frac{30}{4}$

2.2 Equivalent fractions

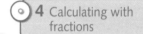

4 Calculating with fractions

- You can simplify a fraction if the numerator and denominator have a common factor.
- To write a fraction in its simplest form, divide the numerator and denominator by their highest common factor.
- **Equivalent fractions** are fractions that have the same value.

Example 3

(a) Complete $\dfrac{2}{3} = \dfrac{}{6} = \dfrac{8}{}$

(b) Write these fractions in their simplest form.

    (i) $\dfrac{10}{16}$ (ii) $\dfrac{24}{36}$

(a)

$$\overset{\times 4}{\underset{\times 2}{\frac{2}{3} = \frac{}{6} = \frac{8}{}}} \quad \text{so} \quad \frac{2}{3} = \frac{4}{6} = \frac{8}{12}$$

(b) (i)

$$\overset{\div 2}{\underset{\div 2}{\frac{10}{16} = \frac{5}{8}}}$$

The highest common factor of 10 and 16 is 2.

(ii)

$$\overset{\div 12}{\underset{\div 12}{\frac{24}{36} = \frac{2}{3}}}$$

The HCF of 24 and 36 is 12.

Exercise 2B

1 Copy and complete these sets of equivalent fractions.

(a) $\dfrac{1}{3} = \dfrac{}{6} = \dfrac{}{12} = \dfrac{}{18}$ (b) $\dfrac{2}{5} = \dfrac{}{10} = \dfrac{}{50} = \dfrac{40}{}$

(c) $\dfrac{3}{8} = \dfrac{6}{} = \dfrac{}{32} = \dfrac{24}{}$ (d) $\dfrac{3}{10} = \dfrac{}{50} = \dfrac{30}{} = \dfrac{}{1000}$

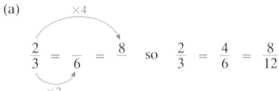

2 Write these fractions in their simplest form.

(a) $\frac{2}{4}$ (b) $\frac{6}{10}$ (c) $\frac{8}{12}$ (d) $\frac{30}{50}$ (e) $\frac{10}{12}$

(f) $\frac{24}{30}$ (g) $\frac{15}{25}$ (h) $\frac{28}{35}$ (i) $\frac{18}{27}$ (j) $\frac{35}{42}$

2.3 Ordering fractions

- To write a list of fractions in order of size
  1 write them all as equivalent fractions with the same denominator
  2 order them using the numerators.

Example 4

Write the following fractions in order, starting with the largest.

$$\frac{1}{3} \quad \frac{2}{5} \quad \frac{3}{10} \quad \frac{1}{6}$$

$$\frac{1}{3} = \frac{10}{30} \qquad \frac{2}{5} = \frac{12}{30} \qquad \frac{3}{10} = \frac{9}{30} \qquad \frac{1}{6} = \frac{5}{30}$$

In order

$$\frac{12}{30} \quad \frac{10}{30} \quad \frac{9}{30} \quad \frac{5}{30}$$

So the order is $\frac{2}{5}, \frac{1}{3}, \frac{3}{10}, \frac{1}{6}$.

Ordering from largest to smallest is writing in **descending order**.

30 is a multiple of 3, 5, 6 and 10.
Rewrite the fractions with a common denominator of 30.

Remember to write the *original* fractions in order for the answer.

Exercise 2C

1 Which is larger

(a) $\frac{1}{4}$ or $\frac{1}{5}$ (b) $\frac{2}{3}$ or $\frac{3}{5}$ (c) $\frac{7}{10}$ or $\frac{11}{15}$ (d) $\frac{6}{7}$ or $\frac{2}{3}$?

2 Write these fractions in ascending order.

$$\frac{1}{2} \quad \frac{2}{5} \quad \frac{3}{10} \quad \frac{1}{4}$$

Use a common denominator of 20.

3 Mia eats $\frac{1}{3}$ of a pie. Ben eats $\frac{1}{4}$ of the same pie. Who eats the larger piece?

4 The seating in a theatre is in four sections. The table below shows what fraction of the seating each section is.

Stalls	$\frac{1}{8}$
Dress circle	$\frac{2}{3}$
Upper circle	$\frac{1}{6}$
Boxes	$\frac{1}{24}$

(a) Which section is the largest?

(b) Which section is the smallest?

5 Write the fractions $\frac{7}{8}, \frac{13}{16}, \frac{1}{4}, \frac{2}{3}$ in descending order.

2.4 Adding and subtracting fractions

- To add or subtract fractions, write them as equivalent fractions with the same denominator.
- To add (or subtract) mixed numbers, add (subtract) the whole number parts, then the fraction parts.

Example 5

Work out
(a) $1\frac{1}{2} + 2\frac{1}{4}$

(b) $3\frac{1}{3} - 1\frac{3}{4}$

(a)
$$1\frac{1}{2} + 2\frac{1}{4} = 3 + \frac{1}{2} + \frac{1}{4}$$
$$= 3 + \frac{2}{4} + \frac{1}{4}$$
$$= 3\frac{3}{4}$$

(b)
$$3\frac{1}{3} - 1\frac{3}{4} = 2 + \left(\frac{1}{3} - \frac{3}{4}\right)$$
$$= 2 + \left(\frac{4}{12} - \frac{9}{12}\right)$$
$$= 1 + \left(\frac{16}{12} - \frac{9}{12}\right)$$
$$= 1\frac{7}{12}$$

You cannot subtract $\frac{9}{12}$ from $\frac{4}{12}$.

$1 + \frac{4}{12} = \frac{12}{12} + \frac{4}{12} = \frac{16}{12}$

Exercise 2D

In this exercise write your answers in their simplest form.

1 Work out
   (a) $\frac{1}{2} + \frac{3}{4}$
   (b) $\frac{2}{5} + \frac{1}{3}$
   (c) $\frac{4}{9} - \frac{1}{4}$
   (d) $\frac{6}{7} - \frac{3}{14}$
   (e) $\frac{3}{5} + \frac{7}{10}$
   (f) $\frac{3}{4} - \frac{2}{7}$
   (g) $\frac{3}{7} + \frac{1}{4}$
   (h) $\frac{7}{8} - \frac{3}{4}$

2 Work out
   (a) $1\frac{1}{4} + \frac{1}{2}$
   (b) $2\frac{2}{3} + \frac{5}{6}$
   (c) $3\frac{2}{3} + \frac{5}{12}$
   (d) $1\frac{1}{6} + 2\frac{1}{3}$
   (e) $2\frac{3}{5} + 3\frac{4}{15}$
   (f) $2\frac{5}{6} + 3\frac{3}{4}$
   (g) $1\frac{1}{2} + 3\frac{2}{7}$
   (h) $3\frac{2}{7} + 2\frac{1}{3}$

3 Work out
   (a) $1\frac{3}{4} - \frac{1}{8}$
   (b) $2\frac{5}{6} - \frac{3}{4}$
   (c) $2\frac{5}{8} - 1\frac{1}{3}$
   (d) $5\frac{9}{10} - 2\frac{1}{5}$
   (e) $3\frac{1}{2} - \frac{3}{4}$
   (f) $5\frac{2}{5} - \frac{7}{10}$
   (g) $4\frac{3}{7} - 2\frac{9}{14}$
   (h) $6\frac{1}{3} - 2\frac{7}{8}$

4 A baby weighs $7\frac{1}{2}$ lb at birth. She puts on $2\frac{3}{4}$ lb in the first month. How much does the baby weigh after one month?

5 Amanda buys $2\frac{1}{2}$ kg of potatoes and $1\frac{3}{8}$ kg of carrots. What is the total weight of vegetables that she buys?

6 A piece of material is $2\frac{3}{4}$ metres long. $1\frac{5}{8}$ metres are needed to make a skirt. How much material is left?

7 A crate filled with bananas weighs $8\frac{3}{4}$ kg. The bananas weigh $6\frac{1}{3}$ kg. How much does the crate weigh?

2.5 Multiplying and dividing fractions

- To multiply two fractions, multiply the numerators then multiply the denominators.
- To divide by a fraction, invert the dividing fraction (turn it upside down) and change the division sign to multiplication.
- To multiply or divide mixed numbers, change them to improper fractions first.

Example 6

Work out

(a) $\frac{2}{5} \times \frac{5}{6}$ (b) $\frac{3}{4} \div \frac{4}{5}$ (c) $1\frac{1}{2} \times 2\frac{3}{4}$ (d) $2\frac{1}{3} \div 1\frac{1}{3}$

(a) $\frac{2}{5} \times \frac{5}{6}$

$= \frac{(2 \times 5) \div 5}{(5 \times 6) \div 5}$

Multiply the numerators and denominators and simplify by dividing top and bottom by 5.

$= \frac{2}{6} = \frac{1}{3}$

(b) $\frac{3}{4} \div \frac{4}{5}$

$= \frac{3}{4} \times \frac{5}{4}$

Invert the dividing fraction and multiply.

$= \frac{15}{16}$

(c) $1\frac{1}{2} \times 2\frac{3}{4}$

$= \frac{3}{2} \times \frac{11}{4}$

Change the mixed numbers into improper fractions.

$= \frac{3 \times 11}{2 \times 4} = \frac{33}{8}$

$\frac{33}{8}$ is an improper fraction; simplify by changing it to a mixed number.

$= 4\frac{1}{8}$

(d) $2\frac{1}{3} \div 1\frac{1}{3}$

$= \frac{7}{3} \div \frac{4}{3}$

Change the mixed numbers into improper fractions.

$= \frac{7}{3} \times \frac{3}{4}$

Invert the dividing fraction and multiply.

$= \frac{(7 \times 3) \div 3}{(3 \times 4) \div 3}$

Simplify by dividing top and bottom by 3.

$= \frac{7}{4}$

$= 1\frac{3}{4}$

This is an improper fraction, simplify by changing it to a mixed number.

Exercise 2E

Write all your answers in this exercise in their simplest form.

1 Work out

(a) $\frac{1}{5} \times \frac{2}{3}$ (b) $\frac{1}{4} \div \frac{1}{2}$ (c) $\frac{2}{5} \times \frac{3}{4}$ (d) $\frac{3}{5} \times \frac{5}{6}$

(e) $\frac{5}{8} \div \frac{3}{4}$ (f) $\frac{11}{16} \div \frac{3}{8}$ (g) $\frac{2}{3} \times \frac{6}{11}$ (h) $\frac{5}{12} \times \frac{4}{15}$

(i) $\frac{3}{8} \div \frac{5}{16}$ (j) $\frac{9}{15} \div \frac{12}{25}$

2 Work out
   (a) $1\frac{1}{2} \times \frac{3}{4}$ (b) $2\frac{1}{5} \times 1\frac{1}{4}$ (c) $3\frac{1}{6} \times 1\frac{2}{3}$ (d) $4\frac{1}{2} \times 3\frac{3}{5}$

   (e) $2\frac{3}{4} \times 1\frac{2}{11}$ (f) $4\frac{2}{5} \times 2\frac{5}{11}$ (g) $5 \times \frac{3}{4}$ (h) $2 \times \frac{3}{8}$

3 Work out
   (a) $1\frac{1}{2} \div 1\frac{3}{8}$ (b) $2\frac{2}{5} \div 1\frac{3}{10}$ (c) $3\frac{1}{3} \div 1\frac{5}{6}$ (d) $2\frac{1}{7} \div 1\frac{3}{14}$

   (e) $5\frac{1}{2} \div 1\frac{3}{4}$ (f) $6\frac{1}{8} \div \frac{3}{4}$ (g) $3 \div \frac{1}{4}$ (h) $5 \div \frac{3}{8}$

4 A plank of wood is 6 m long. It is cut into lengths, each
   measuring $\frac{3}{4}$ m. How many lengths can be cut from the plank?

5 A recipe for a fruit cake requires $2\frac{3}{8}$ kg of fruit. How much fruit
   would be required for three cakes?

6 A gardener spends $4\frac{1}{2}$ hours working on a garden. He spends $\frac{1}{3}$
   of that time weeding. How much time does the gardener spend
   weeding?

7 Karen is writing a book. She writes for $10\frac{3}{4}$ hours during a
   weekend. She takes $3\frac{1}{2}$ hours to write a chapter. How many
   chapters does she write during the weekend?

2.6 Multiplying and dividing decimals by powers of 10

- Decimals are used for parts of a number that are smaller than 1.
- To multiply by 10, move the digits one place to the left.
- To multiply by 100, move the digits two places to the left.
- To multiply by 1000, move the digits three places to the left.
- To divide by 10, move the digits one place to the right.
- To divide by 100, move the digits two places to the right.
- To divide by 1000, move the digits three places to the right.

Powers of 10
$10^1 = 10$
$10^2 = 100$
$10^3 = 1000$
etc.

Example 7

Write down the answers to

(a) 2.36×10 (b) 3.2×1000

(c) $14.3 \div 100$ (d) $3.6 \div 1000$

(a) $2.36 \times 10 = 23.6$ (b) $3.2 \times 1000 = 3200$

(c) $14.3 \div 100 = 0.143$ (d) $3.6 \div 1000 = 0.0036$

Exercise 2F

1 Write down the answers to

(a) 5.31×10 (b) $2.16 \div 10$ (c) $53.58 \div 100$

(d) 2.671×100 (e) 0.36×10 (f) $5.3 \div 1000$

(g) 6.38×100 (h) 0.28×1000 (i) $0.3 \div 100$

(j) $7.86 \div 1000$

2 A book weighs 0.36 kg and has 100 pages.

(a) How much will 10 of these books weigh?

(b) How much does each page weigh?

3 A packet of sweets weighs 113 g. The packet contains 10 sweets. How much does each sweet weigh?

4 How many grams are there in 3.568 kg?

1 kg = 1000 g

2.7 Ordering decimals

- You can sort decimals in order of size by first comparing the whole numbers, then the digits in the tenths place, then the digits in the hundredths place, and so on.

Example 8

Write these numbers in order of size, largest first.

2.03   0.23   0.215   0.013   1.23

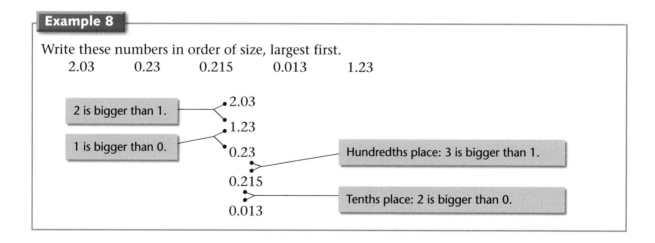

Exercise 2G

1 Write each list of numbers in descending order.

(a) 0.6, 0.62, 6.2, 0.59   (b) 0.76, 0.79, 7.9, 0.079

(c) 3.21, 3.12, 3.27, 0.37   (d) 0.91, 0.09, 1.01, 0.99

(e) 0.02, 0.021, 0.024, 0.002

2 The heights of four children, in metres, are
      Kwame   1.68
      Sunil   1.60
      Tom   1.67
      Rachael   1.52
   Rearrange the list in ascending order of height.

3 In an experiment, the times taken for a chemical reaction to
   occur are
        3.6 s   3.62 s   3.96 s   3.902 s
   Write these times in ascending order.

2.8 Adding and subtracting decimals

- When adding and subtracting decimals make sure you write the
  digits in their correct place value columns.

Example 9

(a) 15.6 + 5.24   (b) 1.3 − 0.24

(a)   15.6   (b) $\overset{2\ 1}{1.\cancel{3}0}$ •——— Fill any gaps
       + 5.24   −0.24   with zero.
       ───────   ──────
         20.84   1.06
          1 •

   Keep the decimal
   points in line.

Exercise 2H

1 Work out
   (a) 5.3 + 2.6   (b) 4.5 + 0.7   (c) 2.13 + 3.14
   (d) 0.32 + 0.49   (e) 1.2 + 1.58   (f) 6.94 + 0.7
   (g) 30.8 + 2.79   (h) 23.1 + 0.23   (i) 5.78 + 0.031
   (j) 21.3 + 0.02

> You should be able
> to add and subtract
> decimals with one
> decimal place mentally.

2 Work out
   (a) 7.8 − 3.6   (b) 6.1 − 2.9   (c) 18.2 − 0.7
   (d) 9.23 − 1.8   (e) 6.2 − 2.34   (f) 2.9 − 0.36
   (g) 15.1 − 1.51   (h) 20.01 − 6.2   (i) 9 − 3.62
   (j) 0.36 − 0.036

3 Kelly is making chicken stew. She uses 1.4 kg of chicken, 0.25 kg
   of onions and 0.625 kg of carrots. What is the total weight of
   these ingredients?

4   A set of triplets weigh 2.3 kg, 2 kg and 2.05 kg at birth. What is their total birth weight?

5   A relay team runs a race. The times for the four runners are 10.02 seconds, 10.3 seconds, 9.98 seconds and 10 seconds. How long does the whole team take to run the race?

6   Harry wants to put his wardrobe, chest of drawers and desk along one wall in his bedroom. The wall is 4.1 m long. The wardrobe is 0.98 m, the desk is 1.4 m and the chest of drawers is 1.75 m. Will they all fit along the wall?

7   Dina is packing for her holiday. Her suitcase weighs 2.6 kg, her clothes weigh 13.7 kg, her shoes weigh 1.3 kg and her toiletries weigh 2.3 kg. Is her packed suitcase within the 20 kg baggage allowance?

2.9 Multiplying and dividing decimal numbers

- When you multiply decimals, the answer must have the same number of decimal places as the total number of decimal places in the numbers you multiply.
- When you divide by a decimal, multiply the number you are dividing by by a power of 10 to change it into a whole number. Then multiply the number you are dividing into by the same power of 10.

Example 10

Work out 0.08×0.14

$$
\begin{array}{r}
14 \\
\times \quad 8 \\
\hline
112 \\
\end{array}
$$
$$_3$$

0.08×0.14

2 d.p. + 2 d.p. = 4 d.p.

The answer must have 4 d.p.

Answer: 0.0112

Example 11

Work out $3.25 \div 0.05$

$$0.05 \overline{)3.25}$$

$\times$ by 100

$$
\begin{array}{r}
6 \; 5 \\
5 \overline{)32\,^25}
\end{array}
$$

$3.25 \div 0.05 = 65$

Example 12

Given that $4.6 \times 2.4 = 11.04$
Write down the value of
(a) 46×240 (b) $110.4 \div 46$

(a) 46×240
    $= 4.6 \times 10 \times 2.4 \times 100$
    $= 11.04 \times 1000$
    $= 11\,040$

(b) $110.4 \div 46$
    $= 11.04 \times 10 \div 4.6 \times 10$
    $= (11.04 \div 4.6) \times 10$
    $= 2.4 \times 10$
    $= 24$

Exercise 2I

1 Work out

(a) 0.3×5 (b) 0.6×0.7 (c) 2.34×0.2

(d) 3.67×0.09 (e) 12.7×0.6 (f) 3.93×1.2

(g) 16.2×3.7 (h) 7.12×0.032

> You should be able to multiply and divide by one decimal digit mentally.

2 Work out

(a) $15.6 \div 6$ (b) $209.2 \div 4$ (c) $28.5 \div 4$

(d) $10.56 \div 0.6$ (e) $2.36 \div 0.8$ (f) $58.6 \div 2.5$

(g) $2.34 \div 0.32$ (h) $3.26 \div 0.16$

3 A piece of fabric 23.4 m long is cut into five equal lengths. How long is each of the lengths?

4 Work out the total weight of eight bags of sun-dried tomatoes weighing 0.225 kg each.

5 A glass holds 0.3 *l*. How many glasses of lemonade can be poured from a 1.5 *l* bottle?

6 A car will travel 17.2 km on 1 litre of petrol. How far will the car travel on 8.5 litres of petrol?

7 How many pens costing £0.79 can be bought with £14.22?

8 Given that
    $5.8 \times 3.2 = 18.56$
Write down the values of
(a) 0.58×0.32 (b) 580×32 (c) $18.56 \div 32$

(d) $1856 \div 0.32$ (e) 0.058×0.0032

2.10 Converting between fractions and decimals

- You can convert a fraction to a decimal by dividing the numerator by the denominator.
- You can convert a decimal to a fraction by writing it as a number of tenths/hundredths/thousandths.
- Not all fractions have an exact decimal equivalent.
- **Recurring decimal** notation:
  - $0.\dot{3}$ means 0.333 333 recurring.
  - $0.\dot{1}\dot{7}$ means 0.171 717 recurring.
  - $0.\dot{1}2\dot{3}$ means 0.123 123 recurring.
- A **terminating decimal** can be written as an exact fraction using a place value table.

Example 13

Convert these fractions into decimals.

(a) $\frac{2}{5}$ (b) $\frac{5}{12}$ (c) $\frac{2}{11}$

(a) $2 \div 5 = 0.4$

(b) $5 \div 12 = 0.416\,666 = 0.41\dot{6}$ —— The 6 repeats.

(c) $2 \div 11 = 0.181\,818 = 0.\dot{1}\dot{8}$ —— Both 1 and 8 repeat.

> If you work out $5 \div 12$ on a calculator, the result on the display could be 0.416 666 7. The result has been rounded to 7 s.f. by the calculator.

Example 14

Convert these decimals into fractions.

(a) 0.6   (b) 0.148   (c) 0.36

(a) $0.6 = \frac{6}{10}$ $\frac{6}{10}$ simplifies to $\frac{3}{5}$ by dividing top and bottom by 2.

$= \frac{3}{5}$

(b) $0.148 = \frac{148}{1000}$ Simplify by dividing top and bottom by 4.

$= \frac{37}{250}$

(c) $0.36 = \frac{36}{100}$ Simplify by dividing top and bottom by 4.

$= \frac{9}{25}$

Example 15

Convert $0.\dot{3}6\dot{1}$ into a fraction.

$s = 0.361\,361\,361\ldots$

$1000s = 361.361\,361\ldots$

Subtract: $999s = 361$

$s = \frac{361}{999}$

> $0.\dot{3}6\dot{1}$ means 0.361 361 361... '361' repeats.

> $\times 1000\ (= 10^3)$ because the decimal has three recurring digits.

Exercise 2J

1 Convert these fractions into decimals.

(a) $\frac{3}{5}$ (b) $\frac{1}{6}$ (c) $\frac{5}{8}$ (d) $\frac{9}{20}$ (e) $\frac{3}{4}$

(f) $\frac{1}{3}$ (g) $\frac{4}{9}$ (h) $\frac{7}{12}$ (i) $\frac{7}{22}$ (j) $\frac{7}{27}$

2 Convert these decimals into fractions. Simplify your answers if possible.

(a) 0.7   (b) 0.5   (c) 0.12   (d) 0.65

(e) 0.875   (f) 0.362   (g) 0.137   (h) 0.685

3 Which of the following fractions have exact decimal equivalents?

(a) $\frac{4}{5}$ (b) $\frac{5}{9}$ (c) $\frac{7}{25}$ (d) $\frac{4}{13}$ (e) $\frac{8}{17}$

4 Find the fraction which is equal to the recurring decimals. Simplify as fully as possible.

(a) $0.\dot{1}$ (b) $0.\dot{6}\dot{3}$ (c) $0.3\dot{1}$

(d) $0.\dot{2}1\dot{6}$ (e) $0.4\dot{5}$ (f) $0.\dot{1}31\dot{4}$

(g) $0.\dot{1}4\dot{7}$ (h) $0.\dot{7}4\dot{0}$ (i) $0.64\dot{2}\dot{3}$

(j) $0.56\dot{1}$

2.11 Ordering decimals and fractions

• To order a mixture of fractions and decimals, first write them all as decimals.

Example 16

Write these numbers in descending order.

$\frac{3}{4}$ 0.82   2.68   3 $\frac{7}{10}$

$\frac{3}{4} = 0.75$ $\frac{7}{10} = 0.7$ | Write the fractions as decimals. |

| 3 is bigger than 2. |

| 2 is bigger than 0. |

• 3

• 2.68

• 0.82

0.75 | Tenths place: 8 is bigger than 7. |

0.70 | Hundredths place: 5 is bigger than zero. |

In descending order: 3, 2.68, 0.82, $\frac{3}{4}$, $\frac{7}{10}$

Exercise 2K

1 Write each list in ascending order.

(a) $0.81, \frac{13}{25}, \frac{8}{10}, 0.84, 0.7$ 　　(b) $\frac{1}{2}, 0.7, \frac{3}{4}, 0.75, 0.73$

(c) $2, 2.3, 2\frac{4}{10}, 2.42, 2\frac{43}{100}$ 　　(d) $\frac{3}{10}, 0.33, \frac{1}{3}, 0.34, \frac{7}{20}$

(e) $4, 4\frac{4}{9}, 4.04, 4\frac{4}{10}, 4.44$

2 Write the measurements in each list in ascending order of size.

(a) The weights of quadruplets at birth
1.3 kg, 1.32 kg, 1.41 kg, 1.39 kg

(b) The times taken for five runners to complete a 100 m race
10.1 s, 10.01 s, 9.92 s, 10.11 s, 9.9 s

(c) The weights of four bags of apples
$\frac{1}{4}$ kg, 0.3 kg, $\frac{1}{2}$ kg, 0.35 kg

(d) The widths of four drill bits
$\frac{3}{8}$ inch, $\frac{1}{4}$ inch, $\frac{1}{6}$ inch, $\frac{2}{5}$ inch

The 100 m world record is 9.77 s, held by Asafa Powell of Jamaica.

2.12 Appropriate degrees of accuracy

- The accuracy of an answer should be appropriate in the context of the question.

Example 17

Billie is organising a conference. Each person attending will get a free pen. 143 people are booked to attend.
Pens are sold in packs of 10. How many packs does Billie need to buy?

$143 \div 10 = 14.3$ packs
Billie needs to buy 15 packs.

> If Billie rounds down, she will have $14 \times 10 = 140$ pens, so 3 people wouldn't have a pen. So she needs to round up.

Example 18

A unit of electricity costs 9.16p. Work out the cost of 234 units.
Give your answer to an appropriate number of s.f.

$234 \times 9.16 = 2143.44$p
Cost = 2143p (4 s.f.) or £21.43.

> You cannot pay 0.44p. Round to the nearest penny.

Exercise 2L

1 A farmer collects 100 eggs from his chickens. How many egg boxes can he fill if an egg box holds 6 eggs?

2 A car transporter is 8 metres long. It is loaded with cars that are 1.8 m long. How many cars can the transporter carry?

3 Burgers are sold in packs of four. Bethan needs 19 burgers for a barbecue. How many packs will she need?

4 Gas costs £0.025 per kW h (kilowatt hour). Edward uses 297 kW h. Calculate the cost of Edward's bill. Give your answer to an appropriate number of decimal places.

5 Samina drives 184 miles in 4 hours. Work out her speed in miles per hour, giving your answer to an appropriate degree of accuracy. Give a reason for your answer.

6 Luisa wants to draw a circle with a circumference of 60 cm. She calculates the radius to be 9.549 296 59 cm. Write down Luisa's answer to an appropriate degree of accuracy. Give a reason for your answer.

7 £20 is shared equally between three children. How much does each child receive? Give your answer to an appropriate number of decimal places.

8 A band receives £0.034 per track downloaded. 17 384 tracks are downloaded. How much does the band receive?

9 A wood supplier has a piece of wood 7 metres long that he wants to cut into six equal lengths. He calculates that each length should be 1.166 67 m long. Explain why this is not a sensible answer.

10 A cook knows that she needs 100 g of flour to make six cakes. She calculates that she needs 133 g of flour to make eight cakes. Explain why this is not a sensible answer. Give a more suitable answer.

2.13 Using a calculator to evaluate expressions

- Make sure you know how to enter calculations involving brackets, powers and roots in your calculator.
- Estimate the solution to a calculation first, so you can check that your answer is sensible.

For more on estimating see Section 1.3.

Example 19

Use your calculator to change these times.
(a) 4 hours 20 minutes to a decimal fraction.
(b) $2\frac{1}{4}$ hours to hours and minutes.

(a) 4 hours 20 minutes $= 4\frac{20}{60}$ hours
$$= 4.333... = 4.\dot{3} \text{ hours}$$
(b) $2\frac{1}{4}$ hours $= 2$ hours and $\frac{1}{4} \times 60$ minutes
$$= 2 \text{ hours and } 15 \text{ minutes}$$

Exercise 2M

Use your calculator to evaluate

1 2.1^2

2 4.3^3

> $\sqrt[4]{2.8561}$ means the 4th root of 2.8561.

3 -2.5^5

4 $\sqrt{6.25}$

5 $\sqrt[3]{54.872}$

6 $\sqrt[4]{2.8561}$

7 $\sqrt{11.1 - 3.81}$

8 $4.2^2 + \sqrt[3]{35} - 6.952$

9 $2.5^2 \times \sqrt{6.8 - 6.44}$

10 $(2.3 + 4.1)^2 + (3.8 + 2.6)^2$

11 $\dfrac{(3.8 + 2.4)^2}{5.1 - 2.6}$

12 $\left(\dfrac{4.5}{2.5}\right)^2$

13 $\sqrt{\dfrac{3.2 + 4.2^2}{0.5}}$

14 $7.8 + \sqrt{\dfrac{9.2 + 1.1}{3.7 + 2.9}}$

15 $\dfrac{3.8 + 4.2^2}{3.4 - \sqrt{2.9}}$

16 Use your calculator to change these times to decimal fractions of hours. The first one has been done for you.

    (a) 1 hour 15 minutes = 1.25 hours

    (b) 3 hours 30 minutes

    (c) 5 hours 12 minutes

    (d) 4 hours 16 minutes

    (e) 11 hours 57 minutes

17 Use your calculator to change these times into hours and minutes.

    (a) 2.25 hours   (b) $3\frac{1}{2}$ hours

    (c) $5\frac{3}{4}$ hours   (d) 4.7 hours

2.14 Percentages, fractions and decimals

- per cent
- %   means 'out of 100'.
- pc
- To change a decimal to a fraction, write it as a fraction with a denominator of 100.
- To change a percentage to a decimal, first change it to a fraction and then to a decimal.
- To change a decimal to a percentage, multiply the decimal by 100%.
- To change a fraction to a percentage, first change the fraction to a decimal then multiply by 100%.

Example 20

Write these percentages as (i) decimals (ii) fractions.

(a) 35%   (b) $37\frac{1}{2}\%$

(a) (i) $35\% = \dfrac{35}{100} = 35 \div 100 = 0.35$

   (ii) $35\% = \dfrac{35}{100} = \dfrac{7}{20}$

(b) (i) $37\frac{1}{2}\% = \dfrac{37\frac{1}{2}}{100} = 37.5 \div 100 = 0.375$

   (ii) $37\frac{1}{2}\% = \dfrac{37\frac{1}{2}}{100} = \dfrac{75}{200} = \dfrac{3}{8}$

Example 21

Write these as percentages.

(a) 0.75   (b) $\frac{4}{25}$ (c) 0.175   (d) $\frac{5}{8}$

(a) $0.75 \times 100\% = 75\%$

(b) $\frac{4}{25} = 4 \div 25 = 0.16$
     $0.16 \times 100\% = 16\%$

(c) $0.175 \times 100\% = 17.5\%$

(d) $\frac{5}{8} = 5 \div 8 = 0.625$
     $0.625 \times 100\% = 62.5\%$

Exercise 2N

1 Write these percentages as (i) decimals (ii) fractions.

   (a) 65%   (b) 20%   (c) 25%

   (d) 32%   (e) 74%   (f) $22\frac{1}{2}\%$

   (g) $67\frac{1}{2}\%$ (h) $33\frac{1}{3}\%$ (i) $66\frac{2}{3}\%$

   (j) $5\frac{1}{4}\%$

2 Write these as percentages.

   (a) $\frac{1}{2}$ (b) 0.6   (c) 0.23

   (d) $\frac{7}{20}$ (e) 0.85   (f) $\frac{3}{10}$

   (g) 0.575   (h) $\frac{9}{40}$ (i) 0.0225

   (j) $\frac{5}{6}$

3 Copy and complete this table of equivalent fractions, decimals and percentages.

Fraction	Decimal	Percentage
		15%
	0.08	
$\frac{7}{10}$		
	0.32	
$\frac{7}{8}$		
		$16\frac{2}{3}\%$
	0.175	

2.15 Finding a percentage of a quantity

- To find a percentage of a quantity, change the percentage to a fraction or a decimal and multiply it by the quantity.

Example 22

Work out
(a) 40% of 80   (b) $22\frac{1}{2}\%$ of £50

(a) **Method 1**   **Method 2**

   40% of 80 $= \dfrac{40}{100} \times 80 = 32$ 40% of 80 $= 0.4 \times 80 = 32$

(b) $22\frac{1}{2}\%$ of £50 $= \dfrac{22\frac{1}{2}}{100} \times £50 = \dfrac{45}{200} \times £50 = £11.25$

Exercise 20

1 Work out
   (a) 30% of 90   (b) 70% of 60   (c) 55% of 20
   (d) 25% of 36   (e) 18% of £10   (f) 36% of £25
   (g) $17\frac{1}{2}\%$ of £50   (h) $52\frac{1}{2}\%$ of 500 kg   (i) $33\frac{1}{3}\%$ of 30 g
   (j) $66\frac{1}{3}\%$ of £27

2 A sailing club has 150 adult members. 52% of the members are women. Find
   (a) the number of women in the sailing club
   (b) the number of men in the sailing club.

3 A yogurt contains 6% fat. Work out how many grams of fat there are in 175 g of yogurt.

4 Lucy earns £21 500 a year. She pays 22% tax. How much tax does Lucy pay on her earnings?

5 A book has 240 pages. 35% of the pages contain photographs. The rest are text only. How many pages in the book are text only?

6 A ticket for a concert costs £27. The performer is paid $16\frac{2}{3}$% of the price of the ticket. How much does the performer receive from each ticket sold?

7 An author is paid $12\frac{1}{2}$% royalties for each of her books sold. Her book is sold for £12. How much does the author receive in royalties per book?

Mixed exercise 2

1 Copy and complete
  (a) $\frac{1}{2} = \frac{}{8}$
  (b) $\frac{3}{4} = \frac{12}{}$
  (c) $\frac{5}{8} = \frac{}{24}$

2 Write these fractions in their simplest form.
  (a) $\frac{10}{15}$
  (b) $\frac{27}{33}$
  (c) $\frac{42}{56}$
  (d) $\frac{36}{48}$

3 Write these mixed numbers as improper fractions.
  (a) $1\frac{3}{4}$
  (b) $2\frac{2}{7}$
  (c) $3\frac{5}{8}$

4 In an office, $\frac{1}{5}$ of the employees go out for lunch, $\frac{3}{4}$ eat lunch at their desk and $\frac{1}{20}$ do not eat lunch.
  (a) What do the largest number of employees do at lunchtime?
  (b) What do the smallest number of employees do at lunchtime?

5 Write the fractions $\frac{1}{3}, \frac{3}{5}, \frac{3}{10}$ and $\frac{5}{6}$ in ascending order.

6 Write down the answers to
  (a) $31.3 \div 10$
  (b) 4.38×10
  (c) $2.56 \div 100$
  (d) 0.2×100
  (e) $5.6 \div 1000$
  (f) 2.13×1000

7 Work out $\frac{2}{3} + \frac{1}{5}$. [E]

8 Work out
  (a) $\frac{2}{3} + \frac{3}{8}$
  (b) $2\frac{1}{5} - 1\frac{5}{6}$
  (c) $\frac{3}{5} \times 3\frac{1}{8}$
  (d) $2\frac{1}{4} \div 3\frac{3}{8}$

9 One DVD weighs 0.125 kg. How much will 100 DVDs weigh?

10 1000 sheets of paper weigh 6.8 kg. How much does one sheet of paper weigh?

11 Work out
  (a) 3.28×1.3
  (b) $4.84 \div 1.1$
  (c) 2.6×32.1
  (d) $0.576 \div 0.16$

12 A packet of cornflakes contains 0.45 kg of cornflakes. A serving of cornflakes is 0.03 kg. Calculate the number of servings in the packet.

13 Carpet costs £14.26 per square metre. Calculate the cost of 5.6 square metres of carpet.

14 Change these fractions into decimals.

(a) $\frac{4}{5}$ (b) $\frac{7}{8}$ (c) $\frac{5}{9}$

15 Change these decimals into fractions in their simplest form.

(a) 0.16   (b) 0.6   (c) 0.485   (d) $0.\dot{5}$

(e) $0.3\dot{8}$ (f) $0.1\dot{3}12\dot{3}$

16 Rearrange these lists of numbers in descending order.

(a) $3.3, \frac{3}{4}, 0.3, 3, \frac{3}{8}$

(b) $\frac{7}{10}, 0.\dot{7}, \frac{3}{4}, 0.77, \frac{37}{50}$

17 Use your calculator to evaluate

(a) 2.7^3 (b) -3.8^2

(c) $\sqrt{14.44}$ (d) $\sqrt[3]{12.167}$

(e) $2.1^2 + \sqrt{3.1} - 1.89$ (f) $\dfrac{(2.1 + 3.2)^2}{3.2 - 1.3}$

(g) $2.4 + \sqrt{\dfrac{2.3 + 2.1}{1.1 - 0.3}}$

18 Electricity costs £0.093 per unit. Catherine uses 343 units of electricity. Calculate the cost of her bill, giving your answer to an appropriate number of decimal places. Give a reason for your answer.

19 Lucy wants to draw a rectangle with an area of 10 cm². She calculates that she could draw a rectangle that measures 3 cm by 3.33 cm. Are Lucy's measurements sensible? Give a reason for your answer.

20 Copy and complete this table of equivalent fractions, decimals and percentages.

Fraction	Decimal	Percentage
$\frac{3}{5}$		
		24%
	0.325	
$\frac{5}{6}$		

21 Work out

(a) 80% of 30   (b) 24% of £10

(c) $12\frac{1}{2}$% of £48   (d) $66\frac{2}{3}$% of 90 g

22 80 girls enter a ballet examination. 85% of the girls pass the
exam. Write down the number of girls who

(a) pass the exam   (b) fail the exam.

23 The cost of a television is £360 plus VAT. The rate of VAT is $17\frac{1}{2}$%.
Calculate the total cost of the television.

24 A department store offers a 15% discount on all sports equipment
on Bank Holiday Monday. A pair of trainers normally costs £85.
Calculate the cost of the pair of trainers on Bank Holiday Monday.

25 Jessica scores 28 out of 35 on her driving theory test. What
percentage is this?

Summary of key points

1 In a fraction:

This number shows how many parts you have.

The top number is called the **numerator**.

$$\frac{3}{4}$$

This number shows the total number of parts there are.

The bottom number is called the **denominator**.

2 A fraction whose numerator is larger than its denominator is called an **improper fraction**. For example, $\frac{5}{2}$ is an improper fraction.

3 An improper fraction can be written as a **mixed number**, with a whole number part and a fraction part. For example, $\frac{5}{2} = 2\frac{1}{2}$ as a mixed number.

4 A mixed number can be written as an improper fraction.

5 You can simplify a fraction if the numerator and denominator have a common factor.

6 To write a fraction in its simplest form, divide the numerator and denominator by their highest common factor.

7 **Equivalent fractions** are fractions that have the same value.

8 To write a list of fractions in order of size
   1 write them all as equivalent fractions with the same denominator
   2 order them using the numerators.

9 To add or subtract fractions, write them as equivalent fractions with the same denominator.

10 To add (or subtract) mixed numbers, add (subtract) the whole number parts, then the fraction parts.

11 To multiply two fractions, multiply the numerators then multiply the denominators.

12 To divide by a fraction, invert the dividing fraction (turn it upside down) and change the division sign to multiplication.

13 To multiply or divide mixed numbers, change them to improper fractions first.

14 Decimals are used for parts of a number that are smaller than 1.

15 To multiply by 10, move the digits one place to the left.

16 To multiply by 100, move the digits two places to the left.

17 To multiply by 1000, move the digits three places to the left.

18 To divide by 10, move the digits one place to the right.

19 To divide by 100, move the digits two places to the right.

20 To divide by 1000, move the digits three places to the right.

21 You can sort decimals in order of size by first comparing the whole numbers, then the digits in the tenths place, then the digits in the hundredths place, and so on.

22 When adding and subtracting decimals make sure you write the digits in their correct place value columns.

23 When you multiply decimals, the answer must have the same number of decimal places as the total number of decimal places in the numbers you multiply.

24 When you divide by a decimal, multiply the number you are dividing by by a power of 10 to change it into a whole number. Then multiply the number you are dividing into by the same power of 10.

25 You can convert a fraction to a decimal by dividing the numerator by the denominator.

26 You can convert a decimal to a fraction by writing it as a number of tenths/hundredths/thousandths.

27 Not all fractions have an exact decimal equivalent.

28 **Recurring decimal** notation:
   ○ $0.\dot{3}$ means 0.333 333 recurring.
   ○ $0.\dot{1}\dot{7}$ means 0.171 717 recurring.

29 A **terminating decimal** can be written as an exact fraction using a place value table.

30 To order a mixture of fractions and decimals, first write them all as decimals.

31 The accuracy of an answer should be appropriate in the context of the question.

32 Make sure you know how to enter calculations involving brackets, powers and roots in your calculator.

33 Estimate the solution to a calculation first, so you can check that your answer is sensible.

34 per cent
   % } means 'out of 100'.
   pc

35 To change a decimal to a fraction, write it as a fraction wth a denominator of 100.

36 To change a percentage to a decimal, first change it to a fraction and then to a decimal.

37 To change a decimal to a percentage, multiply the decimal by 100%.

38 To change a fraction to a percentage, first change the fraction to a decimal then multiply by 100%.

39 To find a percentage of a quantity, change the percentage to a fraction or a decimal and multiply it by the quantity.

3 Index notation and standard form

3.1 Zero, negative and fractional indices

- $x^0 = 1$ for all non-zero values of x
- $x^{-n} = \dfrac{1}{x^n}$ (where $x \neq 0$)
- $x^{\frac{1}{n}} = \sqrt[n]{x}$
- $x^{\frac{m}{n}} = (\sqrt[n]{x})^m$ or $x^{\frac{m}{n}} = \sqrt[n]{x^m}$

x^{-n} is the **reciprocal** of x^n
$x^{-n} \times x^n = 1$

For more on reciprocals see Section 9.1.

Example 1

Find the value of
(a) 3^0 (b) 3^{-2} (c) $16^{\frac{1}{2}}$ (d) $8^{-\frac{1}{3}}$ (e) $8^{\frac{2}{3}}$

(a) $3^0 = 1$

(b) $3^{-2} = \dfrac{1}{3^2} = \dfrac{1}{9}$

(c) $16^{\frac{1}{2}} = \sqrt[2]{16} = +4 \text{ or } -4$

(d) $8^{-\frac{1}{3}} = \dfrac{1}{8^{\frac{1}{3}}} = \dfrac{1}{\sqrt[3]{8}} = \dfrac{1}{2}$

(e) $8^{\frac{2}{3}} = (\sqrt[3]{8})^2 = 2^2 = 4$

The square root of 16 is $+4$ or -4 because
$4 \times 4 = 16$
$-4 \times -4 = 16$
-4 is the **negative square root** of 16.

$8^{\frac{1}{3}}$ and $\sqrt[3]{8}$ mean the cube root of 8.
$\sqrt[3]{8} = 2$ because
$2 \times 2 \times 2 = 8$

Exercise 3A

1 Find the value of
(a) 4^{-2} (b) 8^{-2} (c) 3^{-3} (d) 2^{-4} (e) $36^{\frac{1}{2}}$
(f) $100^{\frac{1}{2}}$ (g) $8^{\frac{1}{3}}$ (h) $1000^{\frac{1}{3}}$ (i) $25^{-\frac{1}{2}}$ (j) $49^{-\frac{1}{2}}$
(k) $27^{-\frac{1}{3}}$ (l) $64^{-\frac{1}{3}}$ (m) 8^0 (n) 2^0 (o) $64^{\frac{2}{3}}$
(p) $8^{\frac{5}{3}}$ (q) $25^{\frac{3}{2}}$ (r) $1000^{-\frac{2}{3}}$ (s) $27^{-\frac{4}{3}}$ (t) $4^{-\frac{5}{2}}$

3.2 Writing numbers in standard form

Standard form is an alternative way of writing very large or very small numbers.

- A number is in **standard form** when it is written like this

$$7.2 \times 10^6$$

This part is a number from 1 up to (but not including) 10.

This part is written as a power of 10, and the power is an integer.

- A number in standard form is $A \times 10^n$ where $0 < A < 10$ and n is an integer.

Example 2

Write in standard form
(a) 35 600   (b) 2 876 000

10^6	10^5	10^4	10^3	10^2	10^1	10^0
		3	5	6	0	0
2	8	7	6	0	0	0

(a) $35\,600 = 3.56 \times 10^4$
(b) $2\,876\,000 = 2.876 \times 10^6$

> The power of 10 is the place value of the first significant figure.

Example 3

Write as ordinary numbers
(a) 2.3×10^3 (b) 3.78×10^5

10^5	10^4	10^3	10^2	10^1	10^0
		2	3	0	0
3	7	8	0	0	0

(a) $2.3 \times 10^3 = 2300$
(b) $3.78 \times 10^5 = 378\,000$

> You can think of multiplying by a positive power of 10 as moving the digits to the left by the same number of places as the power of 10.

Example 4

Write in standard form
(a) 0.48   (b) 0.0025

10^0	10^{-1}	10^{-2}	10^{-3}	10^{-4}
0 .	4	8		
0 .	0	0	2	5

(a) $0.48 = 4.8 \times 10^{-1}$
(b) $0.0025 = 2.5 \times 10^{-3}$

Example 5

Write as ordinary numbers
(a) 2.4×10^{-2} (b) 5.63×10^{-4}

10^0	10^{-1}	10^{-2}	10^{-3}	10^{-4}	10^{-5}	10^{-6}
0 .	0	2	4			
0 .	0	0	0	5	6	3

(a) $0.024 = 2.4 \times 10^{-2}$
(b) $0.000\,563 = 5.63 \times 10^{-4}$

> You can think of multiplying by a negative power of 10 as moving the digits to the right by the same number of places as the power of 10.

A calculator may display the answer to a calculation in standard form.
The display may look like one of these.

Display 1

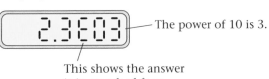

2.3^{03} —— This is the power of 10.

Display 2

$2.3E03$ —— The power of 10 is 3.

This shows the answer
is in standard form.

These displays both show 2.3×10^3.

Make sure you know how to
- read numbers in standard form from your calculator display
- enter numbers in standard form into your calculator.

Exercise 3B

1 Write in standard form
   (a) 800   (b) 7000   (c) 90 000
   (d) 872   (e) 9200   (f) 8700
   (g) 98 400   (h) 834 000   (i) 1 200 000

2 Write as ordinary numbers
   (a) 3×10^2 (b) 5×10^4 (c) 8×10^6
   (d) 2.5×10^4 (e) 3.8×10^6 (f) 2.36×10^4
   (g) 4.78×10^6 (h) 2.94×10^5 (i) 3.84×10^7

3 Write in standard form
   (a) 0.8   (b) 0.72   (c) 0.04
   (d) 0.02   (e) 0.0053   (f) 0.0089
   (g) 0.0032   (h) 0.0485   (i) 0.000 041

4 Write as ordinary numbers
   (a) 2×10^{-1} (b) 3×10^{-2} (c) 5×10^{-4}
   (d) 2.1×10^{-2} (e) 3.4×10^{-5} (f) 5.8×10^{-4}
   (g) 2.38×10^{-6} (h) 4.39×10^{-8} (i) 2.61×10^{-8}

5 Write in standard form
   (a) 456 000   (b) 0.000 34   (c) 16×10^7 [E]

6 Use your calculator to work out
   (a) $2.3 \times 10^4 \times 5$ (b) $4.7 \times 10^{-3} \times 2$
   (c) $5.1 \times 10^6 \times 3$ (d) $8.2 \times 10^{-4} \times 1$

3.3 Calculations using standard form

Example 6

Work out
(a) $(2.3 \times 10^4) \times (3.2 \times 10^3)$

(b) $\dfrac{(5.6 \times 10^4)}{(7.3 \times 10^6)}$

giving your answers in standard form.

(a) $(2.3 \times 10^4) \times (3.2 \times 10^3)$
$= (2.3 \times 3.2) \times (10^4 \times 10^3)$
$= 7.36 \times 10^{4+3}$
$= 7.36 \times 10^7$ ———— Answer is in standard form.

For the index laws see Section 1.7.

(b) $\dfrac{(5.6 \times 10^4)}{(7.3 \times 10^6)} = \dfrac{5.6}{7.3} \times \dfrac{10^4}{10^6}$

$= 0.767\,123\,287 \times 10^{4-6}$
$= 0.767\,123\,287 \times 10^{-2}$ ———— Answer is not in standard form.
$= 7.67 \times 10^{-3}$ (3 significant figures (s.f.))

Example 7

Light travels at a speed of 3×10^8 metres per second.
How long will it take to travel a distance of 7×10^{21} metres?
Give your answer in standard form.

Time $= \dfrac{\text{distance}}{\text{speed}}$

$= \dfrac{7 \times 10^{21}}{3 \times 10^8}$

$= \dfrac{7}{3} \times \dfrac{10^{21}}{10^8}$

$= 2.\dot{3} \times 10^{21-8}$

$= 2.\dot{3} \times 10^{13}$ seconds ———— Answer is in standard form.

Rearranging the formula
Speed $= \dfrac{\text{distance}}{\text{time}}$

Exercise 3C

1 Work out the following.
   Give your answers in standard form.
   (a) $(2.1 \times 10^4) \times (3 \times 10^3)$ (b) $(4.2 \times 10^{-6}) \times (5 \times 10^4)$
   (c) $(8 \times 10^5) \div (2 \times 10^4)$ (d) $(9 \times 10^7) \div (3 \times 10^4)$
   (e) $(3.3 \times 10^{-2}) \times (5 \times 10^4)$ (f) $(4.8 \times 10^4) \div (1.2 \times 10^{-3})$

2 Use your calculator to work out the following.
Give your answers in standard form correct to 3 significant figures.
   (a) $(2.5 \times 10^4) \times (3.8 \times 10^5)$
   (b) $(6.2 \times 10^4) \div (8.4 \times 10^6)$
   (c) $(5.9 \times 10^3) \times (2.4 \times 10^{-3})$
   (d) $(3.54 \times 10^{-3}) \div (2.61 \times 10^7)$
   (e) $(8.92 \times 10^{-2}) \times (3.76 \times 10^{-5})$
   (f) $(1.5 \times 10^7) \div (3.2 \times 10^{-4})$

3 The mass of a neutron is 1.675×10^{-24} grams.
Calculate the total mass of 3.2×10^5 neutrons.
Give your answer in standard form.

4 (a) The speed of light is 3×10^8 metres per second.
How far will light travel in a week? Give your answer in standard form.
   (b) The distance from the Earth to the Sun is 1.5×10^8 km.
How long does it take light to travel from the Sun to the Earth? Give your answer in standard form.

5 The distance from the Earth to the Sun is 1.5×10^8 km.
The distance from Neptune to the Sun is 4.5×10^9 km.
How many times further from the Sun is Neptune than the Earth?

6 The United Kingdom has an area of 2.5×10^5 km^2 and a population of 5.98×10^7 people.
Calculate the number of people per km^2 in the UK.

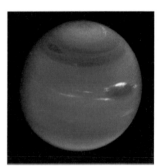

Neptune is the fourth largest planet by diameter and the third largest planet by mass in our solar system.

3.4 Estimating and checking

- You can use standard form to make approximations and estimates.

Example 8

Work out an estimate for
(a) $367\,000 \times 25\,600$
(b) $0.000\,832 \div 0.0392$

(a) $367\,000 \times 25\,600$

$= 3.67 \times 10^5 \times 2.56 \times 10^4$ — Rewrite in standard form.

An estimate is $4 \times 10^5 \times 3 \times 10^4$

$= (4 \times 3) \times (10^5 \times 10^4)$ — Round the numbers to 1 s.f.

$= 12 \times 10^9$

$= 12\,000\,000\,000$

(b) $0.000\,832 \div 0.0392$

$= \dfrac{8.32 \times 10^{-4}}{3.92 \times 10^{-2}}$ — Rewrite in standard form.

An estimate is $\dfrac{8 \times 10^{-4}}{4 \times 10^{-2}}$ — Round the numbers to 1 s.f.

$= \dfrac{8}{4} \times \dfrac{10^{-4}}{10^{-2}}$

$= 2 \times 10^{-4-(-2)}$

$= 2 \times 10^{-2}$

$= 0.02$

Sometimes you do not need to know the exact answer.
Other times you may want to check whether the exact answer given is actually likely to be correct. An estimate does that for you.

Example 9

A tin of emulsion paint says that it covers $19.6\,m^2$. A rectangular room has a perimeter of $13.2\,m$ and a height of $2.8\,m$. Is one tin of paint enough to paint all the walls? If not, how many will be needed?

Number of tins required $= \dfrac{\text{Area}}{19.6} = \dfrac{13.2 \times 2.8}{19.6}$

An estimate is $\dfrac{13 \times 3}{20} = \dfrac{39}{20}$ which is approximately 2.

As you do not paint the door or windows two tins should be enough.

Area of wall $=$
$13.2 \times 2.8m^2$

Example 10

You are on the phone to your stockbroker to sell 623 shares.
He says they sell at £7.92 per share.
Estimate the income from selling these shares.

An estimate is $600 \times 8 = $ £4800.

• One significant figure is accurate enough for most estimating.

However, if the question in Example 10 were 'Will this raise £5000?' you could do $625 \times 8 = $ £5000 in your head as a better estimate.

You have increased the number of shares and the price.
The answer to the question is 'No'.

- When multiplying by a positive number less than 1 the answer will be smaller.
- When dividing by a positive number less than 1 the answer will be bigger.

Example 11

Check, by estimating, if this calculation is correct.
$729 \times 0.93 = 736.56$

$729 \times 0.93 < 729$ | Multiplying by a number less than 1. |
The calculation is wrong.

Actually the number 792 was keyed into the calculator by mistake. This type of error is quite common.

Example 12

Estimate the value of $637 \div 0.87$. Say whether your answer is larger or smaller than the exact answer.

The answer must be greater than 637. •
Estimate $630 \div 0.9 = 700$ •
The exact answer is more than 700 because using 630 instead of 637 makes a smaller answer, and using 0.9 instead of 0.87 also makes a smaller answer.

Dividing by a number less than 1.

Choosing numbers you can do in your head.

Exercise 3D

1 Estimate the value of the following.
  (a) $73\,261 \times 39.478$ (b) $896.25 \times 0.003\,21$
  (c) 638.2×5.987 (d) $0.002\,58 \times 0.794$
  (e) $82.63 \div 0.004\,23$ (f) $15.63 \div 0.0278$
  (g) $9\,300\,000 \div 4187$ (h) $0.000\,28 \div 0.007\,38$

2 Use suitable approximations to estimate the value of the following.
  (a) $\dfrac{28.32 \times 71.9}{5.603}$ (b) $\dfrac{\sqrt{17.3} \times 34.1}{8.26}$

  (c) $(3.19)^2 \times \sqrt{27.9}$ (d) $\dfrac{72.3 + 29.08}{51.2 - 49.3}$

  (e) $\dfrac{18.2}{0.35}$ (f) $\dfrac{58.2}{0.8}$

3 Estimate the value of the following. Say whether your estimate is bigger or smaller than the exact answer.
  (a) $\dfrac{17.6 \times \sqrt{19.32} - 2.19}{0.19}$ (b) $\dfrac{(2.37 - 0.52)^3}{\sqrt{8.231}}$

  (c) $\sqrt{15.3} - (2.1 \times 0.49)$ (d) $\dfrac{(7.836)^2 - (2.092)^2}{\sqrt{7.63} + 18.19}$

4 Estimate how long it takes to travel 423 km at 0.72 km/min.

5 Estimate the value of 217 shares at 43p each.

6 Estimate the cost of 2327 units of electricity at 9.84p per unit.

7 Estimate how long it takes to fill a 100 litre tank at 0.62 litres per second.

8 Estimate how many seconds there are in a week.

9 A plant grows, on average, 0.013 mm/minute.
Estimate (a) how much it grows in an hour,
       (b) how much it grows in a day (24 hours).

Mixed exercise 3

1 Find the value of
  (a) 6^{-2} (b) 8^0 (c) 2^{-3} (d) $49^{\frac{1}{2}}$
  (e) $8^{\frac{1}{3}}$ (f) $27^{\frac{2}{3}}$ (g) $81^{-\frac{1}{2}}$ (h) $25^{-\frac{3}{2}}$

2 Write in standard form
  (a) 3000   (b) 5800   (c) 789 000
  (d) 86 300   (e) 0.5   (f) 0.061
  (g) 0.000 21   (h) 0.000 381

3 Write as ordinary numbers
  (a) 2×10^4 (b) 2.3×10^3 (c) 3.84×10^5
  (d) 8.97×10^7 (e) 3×10^{-4} (f) 2.1×10^{-6}
  (g) 7.92×10^{-3} (h) 8.26×10^{-2}

4 Use your calculator to work out
  (a) $2.68 \times 10^4 \times 3$ (b) $3.82 \times 10^{-5} \times 4$

5 Estimate how many minutes there are in one year.

6 (a) The speed of light is 3×10^8 metres per second.
      How far will light travel in one year? Give your answer in standard form.
  (b) The distance from the Earth to the star Proxima Centauri is 4.068×10^{13} km.
      How long does it take light to reach us from Proxima Centauri? Give your answer in standard form.

7 A colony contains 4×10^9 bacteria. After 24 hours it is 3.2×10^3 times larger.
Calculate the size of the colony after 24 hours.
Give your answer in standard form.

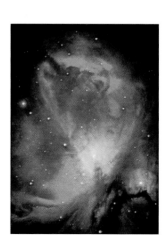

In questions **8–12** give your answers in standard form.

8 Work out the following
   (a) $(4.2 \times 10^3) \times (3 \times 10^4)$ (b) $(8.3 \times 10^{-2}) \times (2 \times 10^5)$
   (c) $(3.6 \times 10^{-2}) \div (1.2 \times 10^{-4})$ (d) $(4 \times 10^4) \div (8 \times 10^2)$

9 The mass of an electron is 9.109×10^{-28} grams.
   Calculate the total mass of 6.4×10^7 electrons.

10 The distance from Neptune to the Sun is 4.5×10^9 km.
   Light travels at a speed of 3×10^8 m/s.
   Calculate the time taken for light to travel from the Sun to
   Neptune.

11 Estimate the value of the following.
   (a) $56\,789 \times 0.023$ (b) $0.378 \times 0.008\,64$
   (c) $8763 \div 0.029$ (d) $0.0078 \div 0.039$

12 The mass of an electron is 9.109×10^{-28} grams and the mass of a
   proton is 1.673×10^{-24} g. Roughly how many times heavier is a
   proton than an electron?

Summary of key points

1 $x^0 = 1$ for all non-zero values of x

2 $x^{-n} = \dfrac{1}{x^n}$ (where $x \neq 0$)

3 $x^{\frac{1}{n}} = \sqrt[n]{x}$

4 $x^{\frac{m}{n}} = (\sqrt[n]{x})^m$ or $x^{\frac{m}{n}} = \sqrt[n]{x^m}$

5 A number is in **standard form** when it is written like this

$$7.2 \times 10^6$$

This part is a   This part is written as
number from 1 up to   a power of 10, and the
(but not including) 10.   power is an integer.

6 A number in standard form is $A \times 10^n$ where $0 < A < 10$ and n is
   an integer.

7 You can use standard form to make approximations and estimates.

8 One significant figure is accurate enough for most estimating.

9 When multiplying by a positive number less than 1 the answer will
   be smaller.

10 When dividing by a positive number less than 1 the answer will be
   bigger.

4 Essential algebra

4.1 Basic rules of algebra

- a means $1a$
- ab means $a \times b$
- $a \times a = a^2$
- A letter or a product of letters and/or numbers is called a **term**. For example $4ab$, $2x^3$
- **Like terms** have the same power(s) of the same letter(s).
- You can add and subtract like terms. For example $a + 2a = 3a$ and $2xy + 3xy = 5xy$
- In an algebraic term, write the number first, then the letters in alphabetical order. For example $2ab$, $\frac{1}{4}xy$.

Example 1

Simplify $5ab - ba$.

$5ab - ba = 5ab - ab = 4ab$

$ba = ab$
and $ab = 1ab$

Example 2

Simplify $2x^2y + 3xy^2 - x^2y$.

$2x^2y + 3xy^2 - x^2y$
$= x^2y + 3xy^2$

$2x^2y - x^2y = x^2y$

Exercise 4A

1 Simplify where possible
  (a) $2x + 3x$
  (b) $5y - y$
  (c) $2ab + 7ab - 3ab$
  (d) $x^2 + 2x^2$
  (e) $2x^2y + 3x^2y$
  (f) $5pq^2 - 3q^2p$
  (g) $3cd^2 + 2dcd$
  (h) $a^24b^3 + b^3a^27$

2 Simplify as fully as possible
  (a) $2a + 3a + 5b - b$
  (b) $x - 3y + 5x + 4y$
  (c) $5p - 2q - 3q - 2p$
  (d) $5a + 2ab - 3bc - a + 4ba + abc$
  (e) $a^2b + ab^2 + 3b^2a - 2ba^2$

4.2 Expanding brackets

- To **expand** an expression, multiply each term inside the brackets by the term outside.
- A − sign outside a bracket changes the sign of every term inside the brackets.

Example 3

Expand these expressions.

(a) $6(x + 4)$
(c) $5x(2x - 7)$
(b) $-3(5x - 2)$
(d) $(3x - 5)x$

$6 \times x + 6 \times 4$

(a) $6(x + 4) = 6x + 24$
(c) $5x(2x - 7) = 10x^2 - 35x$
(b) $-3(5x - 2) = -15x + 6$
(d) $(3x - 5)x = 3x^2 - 5x$

$(-3 \times 5x) + (-3 \times -2)$

Exercise 4B

Expand these expressions.

1 $4(x + 7)$

2 $9(x - 2)$

3 $5(4x + 1)$

4 $2(9x - 4)$

5 $3(7 - 4x)$

6 $x(x + 9)$

7 $x(x - 8)$

8 $x(5x - 4)$

9 $x(2x + 7)$

10 $x(3 - 2x)$

11 $-2(x + 5)$

12 $-7(4x - 1)$

13 $-5(6 - x)$

14 $8x(2x + 7)$

15 $7x(3x - 5)$

16 $4x(3 - 7x)$

17 $-x(2x + 5)$

18 $-9x(2x + 1)$

19 $-3x(5x - 4)$

20 $-2x(8 + 3x)$

21 $-4x(7 - x)$

22 $a(x + 5)$

23 $a(3x - 7)$

24 $5a(2x + 3)$

25 $7a(3x - 5)$

26 $8a(a - 2x)$

27 $(3x + 8)x$

28 $(7x - 5)x$

29 $x^2(2x + 9)$

30 $(5x - 4)x^2$

4.3 Factorising

- **Factorising** is the opposite of expanding.
- When an expression has been **completely factorised**, the terms inside the brackets do not have a common factor.
- To factorise an expression completely, write the highest common factor of the terms outside the bracket.

> ### Example 4
>
> Factorise these expressions completely.
> (a) $5x + 35$ (b) $x^2 - 7x$ (c) $12x^2 + 20x$
>
> (a) $5x + 35 = 5(x + 7)$
> (b) $x^2 - 7x = x(x - 7)$
> (c) $12x^2 + 20x = 4x(3x + 5)$

$12x^2 + 20x = 4(3x^2 + 5x)$ and $12x^2 + 20x = x(12x + 20)$
These are not factorised completely because the terms inside the brackets have a common factor.

The HCF of $12x^2$ and $20x$ is $4x$.

Exercise 4C

Factorise these expressions completely.

1 $6x + 18$ **2** $7x - 28$ **3** $20x + 15$

4 $16x - 24$ **5** $ax + 8a$ **6** $ax - 5ab$

7 $14x^2 + 21$ **8** $27x^2 - 18$ **9** $x^2 + x$

10 $x^2 - 2x$ **11** $8x^2 - 24x$ **12** $35x^2 + 21x$

13 $12x - 18x^2$ **14** $ax^2 - 4ax$ **15** $4ax^2 + 20ax$

16 $30ax^2 - 18ax$ **17** $ax^2 - a^2x$ **18** $12a^2x + 8ax^2$

19 $15a - 20ax^2$ **20** $9a^2x - 21ax^2$

4.4 Simplifying expressions involving brackets

- You can simplify expressions by collecting like terms.

> ### Example 5
>
> Expand and simplify these expressions.
> (a) $5(x + 4) + (3x - 7)$ (b) $4(2x - 1) + 7(x + 3)$
> (c) $4(3x + 1) - (7x - 2)$ (d) $9x - 2(3x - 4)$
>
> (a) $5(x + 4) + (3x - 7) = 5x + 20 + 3x - 7 = 8x + 13$
> (b) $4(2x - 1) + 7(x + 3) = 8x - 4 + 7x + 21 = 15x + 17$
> (c) $4(3x + 1) - (7x - 2) = 12x + 4 - 7x + 2 = 5x + 6$
> (d) $9x - 2(3x - 4) = 9x - 6x + 8 = 3x + 8$

$+(3x - 7)$ means $+1(3x - 7) = +3x - 7$
If there is just a + sign outside the brackets, you remove the brackets.

Exercise 4D

Expand and simplify these expressions.

1 $4(x + 2) + x - 9$

2 $6x - 5 + (3x + 2)$

3 $3(2x - 5) + 2(x + 4)$

4 $5(2x + 3) + 4(2x - 7)$

5 $8 + 3(2x - 5)$

6 $5x - (x + 9)$

7 $7x - (3x - 1)$

8 $8 - (5x + 2)$

9 $6(2x - 5) - 5(x + 3)$

10 $4(3x + 2) - 3(2x - 7)$

11 $8(x + 1) - 4(2x - 3)$

12 $7x - (7x - 9)$

13 $9 - 4(2x + 5)$

14 $11x - 4(3x - 5)$

15 $7x + 12 - 3(x + 4)$

16 $9x - 4(2x - 3) + 1$

17 $x(x - 2) + 5(x - 3)$

18 $x(x + 4) - 7(x - 3)$

19 $x(3x - 4) + 6(2x - 1)$

20 $x(7x - 4) - 2(3x + 5)$

21 $3x(2x - 1) + 4(2x - 1)$

22 $2x(5x + 3) - 5(2x + 3)$

23 $7(x - 1) + 4(x + 5) - 6(x + 3)$

24 $5(2x + 5) - 4(3x - 1) + 2(x - 8)$

25 $12 + 3(4x - 5) - (7x + 8)$

26 $9x - 4(3 - 2x) + 7$

27 $3x - (4x - 9) + 5(2x + 1)$

28 $7(x - 4) + 5 - 3(2x - 1)$

29 $9x + (5x - 4) - 3(4x - 5) - 9$

30 $10 + 3(x - 5) - 5(2x - 1) + 7x$

4.5 Multiplying two expressions with brackets

- $(e + f)(g + h) = e(g + h) + f(g + h)$
  $= eg + eh + fg + fh$

Example 6

Expand and simplify $(x + 4)(x + 7)$.

$(x + 4)(x + 7) = x(x + 7) + 4(x + 7)$
$= x^2 + 7x + 4x + 28$
$= x^2 + 11x + 28$

Example 7

Expand and simplify $(x - 6)^2$.

$$(x - 6)^2 = x(x - 6) - 6(x - 6)$$
$$= x^2 - 6x - 6x + 36 \bullet$$
$$= x^2 - 12x + 36$$

The last term is
$-6 \times -6 = +36$.

Example 8

Expand and simplify $(x + 4)(x - 4)$.

$$(x + 4)(x - 4) = x(x - 4) + 4(x - 4)$$
$$= x^2 - 4x + 4x - 16$$
$$= x^2 - 16$$

- In general: $(x + a)^2 = x^2 + 2ax + a^2$
$(x - a)^2 = x^2 - 2ax + a^2$
$(x + a)(x - a) = x^2 - a^2$ This is called the **difference of two squares**.

Example 9

Expand and simplify $(2x - 5)(4x + 3)$.

$$(2x - 5)(4x + 3) = 2x(4x + 3) - 5(4x + 3)$$
$$= 2x \times 4x + 2x \times 3 - 5 \times 4x - 5 \times 3 \bullet$$
$$= 8x^2 + 6x - 20x - 15$$
$$= 8x^2 - 14x - 15$$

With practice, you should
not need this line of
working.

Example 10

Expand $(3x + 5)(2y - 1)$.

$$(3x + 5)(2y - 1) = 3x(2y - 1) + 5(2y - 1)$$
$$= 6xy - 3x + 10y - 5$$

You cannot simplify this
answer.

Exercise 4E

1 Expand and simplify

   (a) $(x + 3)(x - 5)$ (b) $(x + 4)(x + 3)$ (c) $(x + 2)(x + 8)$

   (d) $(x + 4)(x - 1)$ (e) $(x - 6)(x + 3)$ (f) $(x + 6)(x - 4)$

   (g) $(x - 3)(x - 9)$ (h) $(x - 8)(x + 5)$ (i) $(x - 1)(x - 6)$

   (j) $(x - 8)(x + 8)$ (k) $(x - 6)(x - 2)$ (l) $(x - 12)(x + 12)$

2 Expand

  (a) $(a + 4)(b + 5)$ (b) $(c + 7)(d - 3)$ (c) $(p - 2)(q - 3)$

  (d) $(x - 5)(y + 7)$ (e) $(a - 4)(t - 9)$ (f) $(b + 5)(c - 8)$

3 Expand and simplify

  (a) $(x + 4)^2$ (b) $(x - 1)^2$ (c) $(x + 7)^2$ (d) $(x - 9)^2$

4 Expand and simplify where possible

  (a) $(3x + 2)(x - 3)$ (b) $(2x - 7)(3x + 2)$

  (c) $(4x - 5)(2x - 3)$ (d) $(2x - 7)(y + 2)$

  (e) $(5x - 2)(2x - 7)$ (f) $(5x + 6)(2y - 1)$

  (g) $(3x + 7)(3x - 7)$ (h) $(3x + 9)(4x + 5)$

  (i) $(5x - 9)(5x + 9)$ (j) $(2x + 3)^2$

  (k) $(3x - 5)^2$ (l) $(5x + 1)^2$

  (m) $(7x - 2)^2$ (n) $(2x + y)(5x + 7y)$

  (o) $(4x + 4y)(2x - 3y)$ (p) $(7x - 3y)(2x - 5y)$

  (q) $(5x + 7y)(5x - 7y)$ (r) $(4x - y)^2$

  (s) $(9x - 5y)(2x + 3y)$ (t) $(3x + 5y)^2$

  (u) $(9x + 2y)(9x - 2y)$ (v) $(8x - 3y)^2$

5 Expand and simplify

  (a) $9 + (x - 3)(x + 5)$ (b) $(4x + 3)(x - 2) + 5x - 2$

  (c) $(x + 1)(x - 3) + (x - 8)(x - 4)$ (d) $(x + 7)(x - 3) - (x - 4)(x + 8)$

  (e) $(x + 6)^2 + (x - 1)^2$ (f) $(x + 7)^2 - (x - 4)^2$

  (g) $(x + 5)^2 - (x - 5)^2$ (h) $(5e + 3)^2 - 25e^2$

  (i) $(3x - 4)(3x + 4) - (3x - 4)^2$ (j) $(3x + 1)^2 + 5(2x - 3)$

  (k) $(5x - 2)^2 - 3(2x - 1)$ (l) $(2x - 5)(2x + 5) - (3x^2 - 25)$

4.6 Factorising quadratic expressions

- A **quadratic expression** has the form $ax^2 + bx + c$, where $a \neq 0$,
  - the **coefficient** of x^2 is a
  - the coefficient of x is b
  - the **constant term** is c.

Example 11

Factorise $4x^2 - 7x$.

$4x^2 - 7x = x(4x - 7)$

x is a common factor of $4x^2$ and $7x$.

Example 12

Factorise completely $10x^2 + 15x$.

$10x^2 + 15x = 5x(2x + 3)$

> $5x$ is the HCF of $10x^2$ and $15x$. The terms inside the brackets, $2x$ and 3, do not have a common factor.

Example 13

Factorise $x^2 + 6x - 7$.

> In other words, find two expressions with brackets which have a product of $x^2 + 6x - 7$.

The factors must be
  either $(x + 7)$ and $(x - 1)$
  or $(x - 7)$ and $(x + 1)$.

> The first term in each bracket must be x. ($x \times x = x^2$)
> -7 tells you that the signs in the brackets are different.
> 1 and 7 are the only factors of 7.

$x^2 + 6x - 7 = (x + 7)(x - 1)$

> Expand the brackets to find which pair has a product of $x^2 + 6x - 7$.

Example 14

Factorise $x^2 + 11x + 18$.

> $+18$ tells you that the signs in the brackets are the same.
> $+11x$ tells you that both the signs are $+$.

The factors must be one of these pairs
  $(x + 1)(x + 18)$ $(x + 2)(x + 9)$ $(x + 3)(x + 6)$

> The pairs of factors of 18 are 1×18, 2×9 and 3×6.

$x^2 + 11x + 12 = (x + 2)(x + 9)$

> Expand the brackets until you find the pair which has a product of $x^2 + 11x = 18$.

Example 15

Factorise $6x^2 - 11x + 4$.

> $+4$ tells you that the signs in the brackets are the same.
> $-11x$ tells you that both the signs are $-$.

The factors must be one of these pairs
  $(6x - 1)(x - 4)$ $(6x - 2)(x - 2)$ $(6x - 4)(x - 1)$
  $(3x - 1)(2x - 4)$ $(3x - 2)(2x - 2)$ $(3x - 4)(2x - 1)$

> The first terms in the brackets must be $6x$ and x or $3x$ and $2x$.
> The pairs of factors of 4 are 1×4 and 2×2.

$6x^2 - 11x + 4 = (3x - 4)(2x - 1)$

> Expand the brackets until you find the pair which has a product of $x^2 - 11x + 4$.

Exercise 4F

1 Factorise each of these expressions.

(a) $3x^2 + 5x$ (b) $9x^2 - 12$ (c) $x^2 - 2x$

(d) $21x^2 + 7$ (e) $ax^2 - 5a$ (f) $bx^2 + 3x$

(g) $7x^2 - 28py$ (h) $ax^2 + bx$ (i) $6x^2 - 8y$

(j) $ax^2 + ay$ (k) $8ax^2 - 4by$ (l) $x - 5x^2$

2 Factorise each of these expressions completely.

(a) $5x^2 + 10x$ (b) $9x^2 - 6x$ (c) $12x^2 - 4x$

(d) $15x^2 + 10x$ (e) $ax^2 - 4ax$ (f) $3x^2 + 6bx$

(g) $cx^2 - 2cx$ (h) $ax^2 + ax$ (i) $x^2y + xy^2$

(j) $12xy^2 - 8y$ (k) $8x^2 + 12xy$ (l) $2x^2y^2 - 5xy$

(m) $6x^2y + 15xy$ (n) $10xy^2 - 8x^2y$ (o) $6bx^2 + 3bx$

3 Factorise each of these quadratic expressions.

(a) $x^2 + 4x + 3$ (b) $x^2 - 2x - 3$ (c) $x^2 - 3x + 2$

(d) $x^2 - 6x - 7$ (e) $x^2 - 6x + 5$ (f) $x^2 + 12x + 11$

(g) $x^2 + 2x + 1$ (h) $x^2 - 10x - 11$ (i) $x^2 - 8x + 16$

(j) $x^2 - 7x + 6$ (k) $x^2 - 9x + 20$ (l) $x^2 - x - 20$

(m) $x^2 + 6x + 9$ (n) $x^2 - 20x + 100$ (o) $x^2 + 3x - 10$

(p) $x^2 - 11x - 12$ (q) $x^2 + 8x + 15$ (r) $x^2 - 9x + 14$

(s) $x^2 + x - 30$ (t) $x^2 + 10x + 25$ (u) $x^2 - 3x - 28$

4 Factorise each of these quadratic expressions.

(a) $3x^2 - 4x + 1$ (b) $2x^2 + 5x - 3$ (c) $3x^2 - 18x + 21$

(d) $5x^2 - 12x + 7$ (e) $9x^2 + 12x + 4$ (f) $7x^2 - 35x + 42$

(g) $8x^2 + 18x - 5$ (h) $5x^2 + 28x - 12$ (i) $4x^2 - 40x + 100$

(j) $9x^2 - 24x + 16$ (k) $6x^2 - 13x - 8$ (l) $6x^2 + 9x - 15$

(m) $12x^2 - 23x + 10$ (n) $20x^2 - 60x + 45$ (o) $15x^2 + 11x - 12$

(p) $14x^2 - 9x - 18$ (q) $20x^2 + 32x - 21$ (r) $24x^2 - 28x + 8$

4.7 The difference of two squares

- $x^2 - a^2 = (x + a)(x - a)$

> An expression of the form $x^2 - a^2$, such as $x^2 - 49$, is known as 'the difference of two squares'.

Example 16

Factorise $x^2 - 49$.

$x^2 - 49 = (x + 7)(x - 7)$

> $\sqrt{49} = 7$

Example 17

Factorise $3x^2 - 75$.

$3x^2 - 75 = 3(x^2 - 25)$
$\quad\quad\quad = 3(x + 5)(x - 5)$

3 is a common factor of $3x^2$ and 75.

$\sqrt{25} = 5$

Example 18

Factorise $4x^2 - 49$.

$4x^2 = 2x \times 2x$ and $49 = 7 \times 7$
$4x^2 - 49 = (2x + 7)(2x - 7)$

Exercise 4G

Factorise

1. (a) $x^2 - 4$ (b) $x^2 - 16$ (c) $x^2 - 1$
   (d) $x^2 - 100$ (e) $x^2 - 64$ (f) $x^2 - 144$

2. (a) $5x^2 - 45$ (b) $2x^2 - 72$ (c) $4x^2 - 100$
   (d) $7x^2 - 7$ (e) $3x^2 - 48$ (f) $6x^2 - 24$

3. (a) $9x^2 - 16$ (b) $49x^2 - 9$ (c) $81x^2 - 64$

4.8 Cancelling common factors

- You can simplify **algebraic fractions** by cancelling common factors in the numerator and denominator.

Example 19

Simplify the expression $\dfrac{20a - 15}{5}$.

$\dfrac{20a - 15}{5} = \dfrac{5(4a - 3)}{5}$

$\quad\quad = \dfrac{\cancel{5}(4a - 3)}{\cancel{5}}$

$\quad\quad = 4a - 3$

Factorise the numerator.

Cancel 5s, i.e. divide numerator and denominator by 5.

Example 20

Simplify the expression $\dfrac{6b + 24}{3}$.

$\dfrac{6b + 24}{3} = \dfrac{6(b + 4)}{3}$

$\quad\quad = \dfrac{\overset{2}{\cancel{6}}(b + 4)}{\cancel{3}}$

$\quad\quad = 2(b + 4)$

Factorise the numerator.

$6 \div 3 = 2$

Example 21

Simplify the expression $\dfrac{8ax + 16ay}{2a}$.

$\dfrac{8ax + 16ay}{2a} = \dfrac{8a(x + 2y)}{2a}$

$= \dfrac{\overset{4}{8a}(x + 2y)}{\overset{}{2a}}$

$= 4(x + 2y)$

Factorise the numerator.

$8a \div 2a = 4$

Example 22

Simplify the expression $\dfrac{(c - 4)^2}{(c - 4)}$.

$\dfrac{(c - 4)^2}{(c - 4)} = \dfrac{(c - 4)(c - 4)}{(c - 4)}$

$= c - 4$

Exercise 4H

Simplify these expressions.

1 (a) $\dfrac{4x + 12}{4}$

(b) $\dfrac{9x - 6}{3}$

(c) $\dfrac{16x + 24}{2}$

(d) $\dfrac{30x - 20}{5}$

(e) $\dfrac{21 - 14x}{7}$

(f) $\dfrac{12 - 20x}{2}$

(g) $\dfrac{6x + 15y}{3}$

(h) $\dfrac{24x - 8y}{4}$

(i) $\dfrac{12x + 24y}{6}$

(j) $\dfrac{10ax - 15ay}{5a}$

(k) $\dfrac{16bx + 12by}{2b}$

(l) $\dfrac{10cx - 20cy}{5c}$

2 (a) $\dfrac{(x + 5)^2}{(x + 5)}$

(b) $\dfrac{(3x - 4)^2}{(3x - 4)}$

(c) $\dfrac{(1 - 2x)^2}{(1 - 2x)}$

(d) $\dfrac{4(x - 3)^2}{(x - 3)}$

(e) $\dfrac{7(x + 1)^2}{(x + 1)}$

(f) $\dfrac{2(3x - 7)^2}{(3x - 7)}$

(g) $\dfrac{10(x - 2)^2}{2(x - 2)}$

(h) $\dfrac{15(x + 4)^2}{3(x + 4)}$

(i) $\dfrac{18(2x - 1)^2}{6(2x - 1)}$

(j) $\dfrac{28(2x + 3)^2}{7(2x + 3)}$

(k) $\dfrac{36(5 - 4x)^2}{9(5 - 4x)}$

(l) $\dfrac{18(4 - 5x)^2}{12(4 - 5x)}$

4.9 Adding and subtracting algebraic fractions

- To add or subtract the algebraic fractions $\frac{1}{m}$ and $\frac{1}{n}$, change them to equivalent fractions with denominator mn.

$mn = m \times n$

Example 23

Write as a single fraction in its lowest terms.

(a) $\dfrac{2}{x} + \dfrac{1}{y}$

(b) $\dfrac{2}{3(x+1)^2} - \dfrac{1}{x+1}$

(a) $\dfrac{2}{x} + \dfrac{1}{y}$

$= \dfrac{2y + x}{xy}$

(b) $\dfrac{2}{3(x+1)^2} - \dfrac{1}{x+1}$

$= \dfrac{2}{3(x+1)^2} - \dfrac{1 \times 3(x+1)}{3(x+1)^2}$

$= \dfrac{2 - 3x - 3}{3(x+1)^2}$

$= \dfrac{-1 - 3x}{3(x+1)^2}$

> $3(x+1)^2$ and $(x+1)$ have a common factor $(x+1)$.

Exercise 4I

Write each expression as a single fraction in its lowest terms.

1 $\dfrac{x}{3} + \dfrac{2x}{3}$

2 $\dfrac{3}{x} + \dfrac{5}{7x}$

3 $\dfrac{x+1}{3} + \dfrac{x+3}{5}$

4 $\dfrac{3}{x+1} + \dfrac{4}{x+2}$

5 $\dfrac{1}{y} - \dfrac{1}{4-y}$

6 $\dfrac{1}{4} + \dfrac{5}{2y-3}$

7 $\dfrac{3}{x-1} + \dfrac{4}{2(x+1)^2}$

8 $\dfrac{3}{x^2} - \dfrac{1}{x(x-2)}$

4.10 Multiplying and dividing algebraic fractions

Example 24

Simplify fully $\dfrac{5x+15}{x^2+3x-4} \times \dfrac{x^2-2x+1}{x^2-9}$

$\dfrac{5x+15}{x^2+3x-4} \times \dfrac{x^2-2x+1}{x^2-9} = \dfrac{5(x+3)}{(x+4)(x-1)} \times \dfrac{(x-1)^2}{(x+3)(x-3)}$

$\dfrac{5(\cancel{x+3})}{(x+4)(\cancel{x-1})} \times \dfrac{(x-1)^{\cancel{2}}}{(\cancel{x+3})(x-3)} = \dfrac{5(x-1)}{(x+4)(x-3)}$

> Factorise all expressions completely.

> Cancel $(x+3)$ and $(x-1)$.

- Dividing by an algebraic fraction is equivalent to multiplying by its reciprocal.

Example 25

Simplify fully $\dfrac{x^2 - x - 12}{x^2 + 10x + 25} \div \dfrac{2x - 8}{x^2 - 25}$.

$$\dfrac{x^2 - x - 12}{x^2 + 10x + 25} \div \dfrac{2x - 8}{x^2 - 25} = \dfrac{x^2 - x - 12}{x^2 + 10x + 25} \times \dfrac{x^2 - 25}{2x - 8}$$

Invert the second fraction and change $\div$ to $\times$.

$$\dfrac{x^2 - x - 12}{x^2 + 10x + 25} \times \dfrac{x^2 - 25}{2x - 8} = \dfrac{(x - 4)(x + 3)}{(x + 5)^2} \times \dfrac{(x + 5)(x - 5)}{2(x - 4)}$$

Factorise all expressions completely.

$$\dfrac{(x - 4)(x + 3)}{(x + 5)^2} \times \dfrac{(x + 5)(x - 5)}{2(x - 4)} = \dfrac{(x + 3)(x - 5)}{2(x + 5)}$$

Cancel $(x - 4)$ and $(x + 5)$.

Exercise 4J

Simplify these expressions fully.

1 $\dfrac{3x^2 - 12x}{x^2 + 2x}$

2 $\dfrac{4x^2 + 4x}{2x^2 - 10x}$

3 $\dfrac{x^2 + x - 6}{x^2 - 4x + 4}$

4 $\dfrac{7x^2 - 35x}{x^2 - x - 20}$

5 $\dfrac{x^2 + 2x + 1}{x^2 - 1}$

6 $\dfrac{x^2 + 5x - 6}{4x + 24}$

7 $\dfrac{2x^2 - 32}{x^2 - 3x - 4}$

8 $\dfrac{x^2 - 10x + 25}{x^2 + x - 30}$

9 $\dfrac{x^2 - 6x}{x + 4} \times \dfrac{5x + 20}{x}$

10 $\dfrac{3x + 6}{x + 1} \times \dfrac{x^2 - 1}{4x + 8}$

11 $\dfrac{x^2 + 6x + 5}{x^2 + x} \times \dfrac{6x}{2x + 10}$

12 $\dfrac{x^2 - 14x + 49}{x^2 - 9x + 14} \times \dfrac{x^2 - 2x}{x^2 - 49}$

13 $\dfrac{x^2 - 2x - 24}{x^2} \div \dfrac{5x - 30}{x}$

14 $\dfrac{x^2 + 10x + 25}{5x - 10} \div \dfrac{x^2 + 4x - 5}{2x^2 - 4x}$

15 $\dfrac{x^2 - 64}{x^2 + 2x + 1} \div \dfrac{x^2 - 16x + 64}{x^2 - 7x - 8}$

16 $\dfrac{2x^2 - 7x - 15}{x^2 + 1} \div \dfrac{8x + 12}{8x^2 + 8}$

Mixed exercise 4

1 Expand these expressions.

(a) $8(x + 5)$
(b) $7(3x - 4)$
(c) $5(1 - 6x)$
(d) $x(9x - 2)$
(e) $-4(2x + 5)$
(f) $6x(x - 3)$
(g) $-2x(5x - 7)$
(h) $a(8x + 3a)$
(i) $(9 - 4x)x$

2 Factorise these expressions completely.

(a) $9x - 27$ (b) $28x + 21$ (c) $10x^2 - 20$

(d) $x^2 - x$ (e) $32x^2 + 40x$ (f) $24x + 16x^2$

(g) $ax^2 - bx$ (h) $6ax^2 - 9ax$ (i) $25ax - 15ax^2$

3 (a) Expand $3(4x - 5)$.

(b) Factorise $5y + 40$.

(c) Simplify $3a + 7b + 9a + 4b$.   [E]

4 (a) Simplify $x^4 \div x^9$.

(b) Simplify $3w^5y^2 \times 4w^3y^4$.   [E]

5 Expand and simplify these expressions.

(a) $7(x - 3) + (2x - 1)$ (b) $6(2x + 3) + 5(3x - 4)$

(c) $4(3x - 5) - (7x - 9)$ (d) $2(7x + 4) - 3(2x + 1)$

(e) $9 - 5(3x - 2)$ (f) $11x + 5(2 - 3x)$

(g) $x(x + 9) - 4(x - 2)$ (h) $6(2 - 3x) + 5 - 8(1 - 2x)$

6 Expand and simplify

(a) $(x + 9)(x + 2)$ (b) $(x - 1)(x + 7)$ (c) $(x - 8)(x - 2)$

(d) $(x + 5)(x - 3)$ (e) $(x - 3)(x + 3)$ (f) $(x - 4)^2$

(g) $(x + 8)^2$ (h) $(x - 7)(2x + 5)$ (i) $(4x - 1)(2x - 3)$

(j) $(3x - 1)(3x + 1)$ (k) $(3x - 1)^2$ (l) $(4x + 7)^2$

(m) $(2x - y)(5x + 2y)$ (n) $(5x - 4y)^2$ (o) $(3x + 4y)(3x - 4y)$

7 Factorise each of these expressions completely.

(a) $12a^2 - 9a$ (b) $ab^2 - 7ab$ (c) $15ab^2 + 20a$

(d) $6c^2 + 2c$ (e) $3pq^2 - 2pq$ (f) $24xy^2 + 18x^2y$

8 Factorise

(a) $x^2 - 81$ (b) $5x^2 - 20$

(c) $8x^2 - 32$ (d) $9x^2 - 9$

9 (a) Factorise $x^2 - 3x$.

(b) Simplify $k^5 \div k^2$.

(c) Expand and simplify   (i) $4(x + 5) + 3(x - 7)$

                           (ii) $(x + 3y) + (x + 2y)$

(d) Factorise $(p + q)^2 + 5(p + q)$.   [E]

10 Simplify these expressions.

(a) $\dfrac{25x + 15}{5}$ (b) $\dfrac{16x - 40}{8}$ (c) $\dfrac{21ax + 12ay}{3a}$

(d) $\dfrac{(x - 2)^2}{(x - 2)}$ (e) $\dfrac{20(x + 8)^2}{4(x + 8)}$ (f) $\dfrac{36(3x - 8)^2}{4(3x - 8)}$

11 Factorise each of these quadratic expressions.

   (a) $x^2 + 8x + 7$ (b) $x^2 + x - 2$ (c) $x^2 - 7x + 12$

   (d) $x^2 - 64$ (e) $x^2 - 7x - 18$ (f) $x^2 - 18x + 81$

   (g) $3x^2 - 108$ (h) $3x^2 - 19x + 20$ (i) $16x^2 - 1$

   (j) $12x^2 - 13x - 4$ (k) $4x^2 - 28x + 49$ (l) $20x^2 - 27x - 8$

12 (a) Simplify $a^3 \times a^4$.

   (b) Simplify $3x^2y \times 5xy^3$.

   (c) Simplify $\dfrac{(x-1)^2}{x-1}$.

   (d) Factorise $a^2 - 9b^2$.

13 Simplify these expressions fully.

   (a) $\dfrac{8x^2 - 8x}{x^2 + 3x - 4}$ (b) $\dfrac{x^2 - 6x + 9}{5x^2 - 45}$ (c) $\dfrac{x^2 - 3x - 10}{x^2 - 6x + 5}$

   (d) $\dfrac{x^2 - 9x + 14}{x^2 - 6x - 7}$ (e) $\dfrac{x}{3(x+2)(x+3)} - \dfrac{1}{5(x+3)}$

   (f) $\dfrac{3}{x^2 - 9} + \dfrac{2}{x+3}$

   (g) $\dfrac{6x - 24}{x^2 - 25} \times \dfrac{x+5}{3x - 12}$

   (h) $\dfrac{x^2 - 6x - 16}{x^2 - 4x - 32} \times \dfrac{x^2 + 8x + 16}{x^2 + 2x}$

   (i) $\dfrac{8x - 40}{x^2 + 6x - 7} \div \dfrac{6x - 30}{x^2 - 1}$

   (j) $\dfrac{x^2 - 20x + 100}{x^2 - 6x - 7} \div \dfrac{x^2 - 100}{x^2 - 9x + 14}$

Summary of key points

1 a means $1a$

2 ab means $a \times b$

3 $a \times a = a^2$

4 A letter or a product of letters and/or numbers is called a **term**. For example $4ab$, $2x^3$

5 **Like terms** have the same power(s) of the same letter(s).

6 You can add or subtract like terms. For example $a + 2a = 3a$ and $2xy + 3xy = 5xy$

7 In an algebraic term, write the number first, then the letters in alphabetical order. For example $2ab$ or $\frac{1}{4}xy$.

8 To **expand** an expression, multiply each term inside the brackets by the term outside.

9 A $-$ sign outside a bracket changes the sign of every term inside the brackets.

10 **Factorising** is the opposite of expanding.

11 When an expression has been **completely factorised**, the terms inside the brackets do not have a common factor.

12 To factorise an expression completely, write the highest common factor of the terms outside the bracket.

13 You can simplify expressions by collecting like terms.

14 $(e + f)(g + h) = e(g + h) + f(g + h)$
$$= eg + eh + fg + fh$$

15 In general: $(x + a)^2 = x^2 + 2ax + a^2$
$$(x - a)^2 = x^2 - 2ax + a^2$$
$(x + a)(x - a) = x^2 - a^2$. This is called the **difference of two squares**.

16 A **quadratic expression** has the form $ax^2 + bx + c$, where $a \neq 0$,
  ○ the **coefficient** of x^2 is a
  ○ the coefficient of x is b
  ○ the **constant term** is c.

17 You can simplify **algebraic fractions** by cancelling common factors in the numerator and denominator.

18 To add or subtract the algebraic fractions $\frac{1}{m}$ and $\frac{1}{n}$, change them to equivalent fractions with denominator mn.

19 Dividing by an algebraic fraction is equivalent to multiplying by its reciprocal.

5 Coordinates and graphs

5.1 Coordinates in all four quadrants

- The x- and y-axes can both be extended to include negative numbers. Coordinates can include positive and negative numbers.
- The x- and y-axes divide the coordinate grid into four **quadrants**.

Example 1

What are the coordinates of the points A, B and C on the grid?

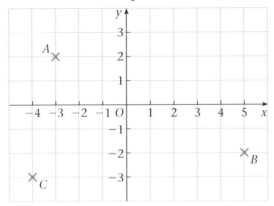

A is $(-3, 2)$, B is $(5, -2)$, C is $(-4, -3)$.

Exercise 5A

1   Write down the coordinates of the points marked on the grid.

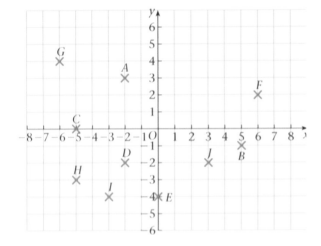

2 Plot the following points on a grid. The grid needs to go from
-6 to $+6$ in each direction.

$A(-3, 0)$ $\quad$ $B(-4, 5)$ $\quad$ $C(5, -4)$ $\quad$ $D(-4, -5)$

$E(3, -3)$ $\quad$ $F(-2, 6)$ $\quad$ $G(-3, -1)$ $\quad$ $H(0, -5)$

5.2 Coordinates to complete shapes

Example 2

Give the coordinates of the points that could complete the
parallelogram in the diagram.

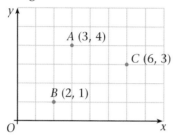

1 Suppose *BA* is a side of the parallelogram.
This is 1 unit across (*x*-direction) and 3 up (*y*-direction).
CD must also be 1 across and 3 up.
D is (7, 6).

There are three possible
answers.

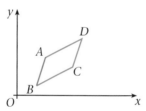

2 If *AB* is a side then *A* to *B* is 1 unit left and 3 down.
C to *D* must also be 1 left and 3 down. *D* is (5, 0).

For more on the
properties of a
parallelogram see
Section 7.5.

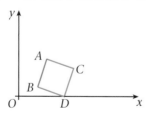

3 There is another possibility: *CB* is a side of the parallelogram.
C to *B* is 4 units left and 2 down.
This means *D* would be $(-1, 2)$.

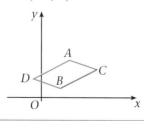

Exercise 5B

1 Copy each diagram and find a point to complete an isosceles triangle. Find one where the given line is one of the equal sides and one where it is the unequal side.
Are there any others?

(a)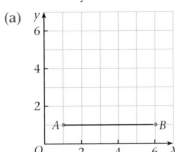

(b)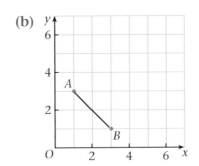

(c)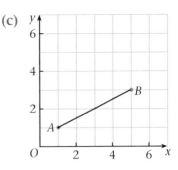

2 Draw axes which run 0–8 for x and 0–6 for y.
Plot $A(2, 3)$, $B(4, 3)$ and $C(5, 1)$.
Find three points which could complete a parallelogram.

3 Draw axes running from 0 to 6 on both axes.
Plot points $P(2, 4)$ and $Q(4, 3)$.
These are two vertices of a square.
Find three pairs of points which could complete the square.

4 Draw the x-axis to run from 0 to 8 and the y-axis from 0 to 5.
Plot points $A(7, 1)$, $B(2, 1)$ and $C(1, 3)$.
Find the coordinates of D to complete trapezium $ABCD$.

> For more on the properties of a trapezium see Section 7.5.

5 Draw the x-axis from -10 to $+10$ and the y-axis from -8 to $+6$.
Plot points $A(-3, 5)$, $B(-8, 0)$ and $C(-7, -7)$.
(a) Find the coordinates of D to complete the rhombus.
(b) Find four pairs of integer coordinates that would complete a kite.

> For more on the properties of a rhombus or kite see Section 7.5.

5.3 Mid-points of line segments

- The **mid-point** of the line segment joining (a, b) and (c, d) is
$$\left(\frac{a + c}{2}, \frac{b + d}{2}\right)$$

> A line can continue for ever. The part of the line between points A and B is called the **line segment** AB.

Example 3

The points A, B and C have these coordinates
    A is $(1, 1)$, B is $(4, 3)$ and C is $(2, 6)$
$ABCD$ is a square.

(a) Find the coordinates of D.
(b) Find the coordinates of the mid-points of AC and BD.

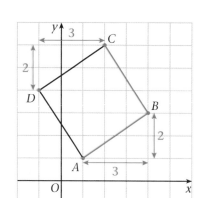

Draw the grid and three points A, B, C.

(a) *D* is (−1, 4).

The shift from *A* to *B* is 3 right, 2 up.
So the shift from *C* to *D* must be 3 left, 2 down.

(b) *A* is (1, 1)   *C* is (2, 6)

The mid-point of *AC* is

$$\left(\frac{1+2}{2}, \frac{1+6}{2}\right) = \left(\frac{3}{2}, \frac{7}{2}\right) \text{ or } (1\tfrac{1}{2}, 3\tfrac{1}{2})$$

The mid-point of *BD* is

$$\left(\frac{-1+4}{2}, \frac{4+3}{2}\right) = (1\tfrac{1}{2}, 3\tfrac{1}{2})$$

The mid-point of *AC* is the same point as the mid-point of *BC*. This shows that the two diagonals of a square bisect each other.

Exercise 5C

1 The diagram shows a triangle *ABC*.

(a) Write down the coordinates of
  (i) point *A*
  (ii) point *B*
  (iii) point *C*.

(b) *ABCD* is a parallelogram.
   Find the coordinates of *D*.

(c) Find the coordinates of the mid-point of
  (i) *AC*
  (ii) *CD*.

(d) Write down the equation of the line *AC*.

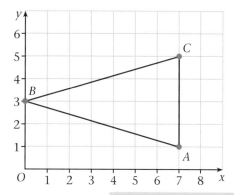

For more on equations of lines see Section 5.5.

2 Draw a coordinate grid for *x* and *y* from −8 to +8.

(a) Plot the points *A*(4, 6), *B*(1, 3), *C*(6, 6), *D*(8, 6), *E*(4, −2),
   F(−2, 4), *G*(−4, −6), *H*(−5, 3).

(b) Find the coordinates of the mid-points of the line segments
   AC, *AE*, *EF*, *FH*, *EG*, *FH* and *BH*.

3 Find the mid-point of

(a) the line segment joining (3, −2) to (−4, 3)

(b) the line segment joining (−2, −6) to (3, 5).

4 The point (5, 6) is the mid-point of the line segment *AB*.
   A is the point (2, 1).
   Find the coordinates of *B*.

5.4 1-D, 2-D or 3-D?

● 13 3-D coordinates on shapes

- The number line goes in one direction.
  It is **one-dimensional** (**1-D** for short).
- The coordinates on a grid go in two directions. They cover a flat shape which is **two-dimensional** (**2-D** for short).
- Solid shapes, space and volumes are **three-dimensional** (**3-D** for short). To describe positions in space a third axis is used. This is the z-axis. 3-D coordinates look like this (4, 5, 7).

(4, 5, 7) means
4 units in the x-direction
5 units in the y-direction
7 units in the z-direction.

Example 4

Write down the coordinates of points A, B, C, D of this cuboid.

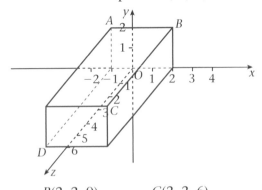

$A(-1, 2, 0)$ $B(2, 2, 0)$ $C(2, 2, 6)$ $D(-1, 0, 6)$

−1 in the x-direction
2 in the y-direction
0 in the z-direction

2 in the x-direction
2 in the y-direction
6 in the z-direction

Exercise 5D

1　List these shapes in a table with headings '2-D' and '3-D'.

　　　pentagon, pyramid, hexagon, triangle, cylinder, cone, trapezium, cuboid, rectangle, sphere, square, circle

2　Make a list of the three-dimensional coordinates from the following.

　　　(1, 4, 2)　(3, 3)　(6.2, 1, 4)　(0, 3)　(2, 3, 4)　(4, 5, 0)
　　　(6, 0, 7)　(6, 3)　(3)　(−3, 0, 0)

3　Write down all the coordinates of each vertex of this cuboid.

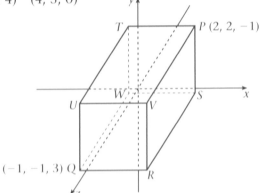

5.5 Graphs of straight lines parallel to the axes

- Lines parallel to the x-axis have equation $y = $ a constant.
- Lines parallel to the y-axis have equation $x = $ a constant.

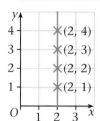

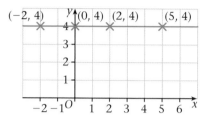

The x-coordinate for all points on this line is 2.
The equation of this line is $x = 2$.

The y-coordinate for all points on this line is 4.
The equation of this line is $y = 4$.

Example 5

(a) Write down the equations of lines P, Q and R.
(b) Draw the line with equation $y = -2$.

(a)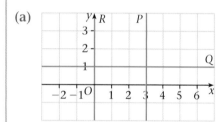

P is $x = 3$

All points on P have x-coordinate 3.

Q is $y = 1$

All points on Q have y-coordinate 1.

R is $x = 0$.

All points on R have x-coordinate 0.

(b)

Plot three points with y-coordinate −2.

Two points is enough but plot three as a check.

Exercise 5E

1 Write down the equations of the lines shown on the graph.

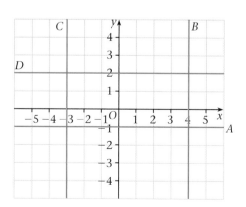

2 On a graph, draw lines with equation
   (a) $y = 2$
   (b) $y = 5$
   (c) $y = 0$
   (d) $y = -1\frac{1}{2}$.
   What do you notice about these lines?

5.6 Straight lines passing through the origin

- The equation of the straight line passing through (0, 0), such that for each point on the line the x-coordinate equals the y-coordinate, is

  $y = x$

  > The **origin** is the point (0, 0).

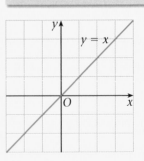

- The equation of the straight line passing through (0, 0), such that for each point on the line the x-coordinate equals the negative of the y-coordinate, is

  $y = -x$

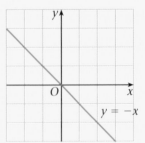

- The equation of any straight line passing through (0, 0) is always either

  $y = $ a positive number times x ($y = ax$)

  or

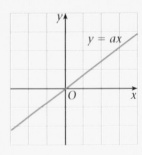

  $y = $ a negative number times x ($y = -ax$)

  Remember $x = 0$ is the y-axis and $y = 0$ is the x-axis.
  Both these lines pass through (0, 0).

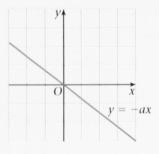

Example 6

Write down the equation of this line.

The equation is $y = ax$ for some value of a.

the line passes through $(-1, -3)$, $(0, 0)$ and $(2, 6)$.

For each point the y-coordinate is 3 times the x-coordinate.

The equation is $y = 3x$.

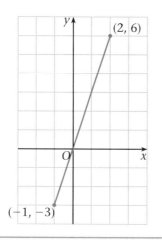

Look for a relationship between the x- and y-coordinates for each point.

Exercise 5F

1 (a) Plot the points with coordinates
$(0, 0)$ $(1, 1)$ $(2, 2)$ $(3, 3)$ $(-5, -5)$

(b) Join these points with a straight line.

(c) Write down the equation of the straight line.

Draw a grid from -6 to $+6$ on both axes.

2 Write down the equation of the line marked L.

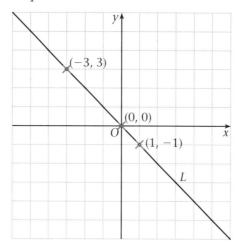

3 Draw a coordinate grid with both axes from -8 to 8.
Draw the line with equation $y = 5x$.

When $x = 1$, $y = 5 \times 1 = 5$.

4 (a) Choose at least three different positive values of a and draw the graphs of $y = ax$.
Write down anything you notice about your lines.

(b) Choose at least three different negative values of a and draw the graphs of $y = ax$.
How are these different from your graphs in part (a)?

5 (a) Plot the points with coordinates
        (0, 0)   (3, 6)   (−2, −4)

   (b) Join these points with a straight line.

   (c) Find the equation of this straight line.

6 (a) Plot the points with coordinates
        (0, 0)   (1, −3)   (−2, 6)

   (b) Join these points with a straight line.

   (c) Find the equation of this straight line.

5.7 Graphs of linear functions

○) 9 Drawing straight
   lines

Example 7

Draw the graph of $y = 2x + 2$ taking values of x from −3 to 2.

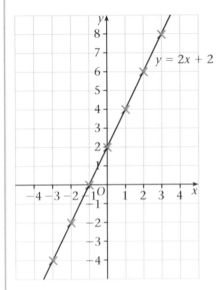

$y = 2x + 2$

x	−3	−2	−1	0	1	2
y	−4	−2	0	2	4	6

Draw up a table of values.

• $y = 2x + 2$ is the equation of a straight line. The coordinates of any
  point on the straight line satisfy the equation $y = 2x + 2$.

• In general, $y = mx + c$ is the equation of a straight line. m may be
  positive or negative, a whole number or a fraction.

For example, $y = -2x + 1$
and $y = \frac{1}{2}x - 5$ are
equations of straight lines.

Example 8

Draw the graph of $y = -2x + 1$, taking values of x from -2 to 3.

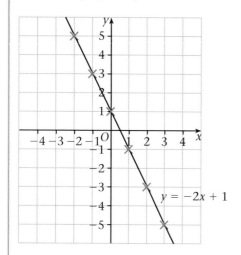

x	-2	-1	0	1	2	3
y	5	3	1	-1	-3	-5

- The equation $y = -2x + 1$ may also be written as $y = 1 - 2x$ or $2x + y = 1$.

- You only need to plot two points on a line to be able to draw it, but a third point is a useful check.

Choose numbers which make your working out as easy as possible!

Example 9

Draw the graph of $x + y = 3$, for values of x from -2 to 5.

Extend the line to $x = -2$ and $x = 5$.

For every point on the line $x + y = 3$, the sum of the x-coordinate and the y-coordinate is 3.

x	0	2	3
y	3	1	0

So, when $x = 0$, $y = 3$
when $x = 3$, $y = 0$
when $x = 2$, $y = 1$

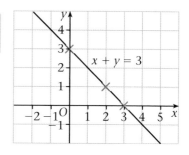

Choose 'easy' values.
Include $x = 0$ and $y = 0$.

- The equation $x + y = 3$ may also be written as $y = -x + 3$ or $y = 3 - x$.

Example 10

Draw the graph of $2x + 3y = 12$ for values of x from -2 to 8.

x	0	3	6
y	4	2	0

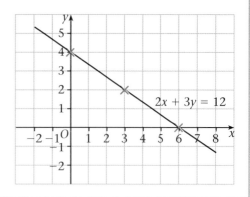

- The equation $2x + 3y = 12$ may also be written as $y = -\frac{2}{3}x + 4$.

Exercise 5G

1 Copy and complete the table of values for $y = 3x - 2$ and draw its graph.

x	-3	-2	-1	0	1	2	3
y		-8					7

2 Copy and complete the table of values for $y = \frac{1}{2}x + 2$ and draw its graph.

x	-6	-4	-2	0	2	4	6
y			1				5

3 Copy and complete the table of values for $x + y = 5$ and draw its graph.

x	-2	-1	0	1	2	3	4	5	6
y		6							

4 Copy and complete the table of values for $x - y = 1$ and draw its graph.

x	-2	-1	0	1	2	3	4	5	6
y		-2							

5 Copy and complete the table of values for $x + 2y = 6$ and draw its graph.

x	-4	-2	0	2	4	6	8	10
y		4						

6 Copy and complete the table of values for $3x + 4y = 12$ and draw its graph.

x	-4	0	4	8	12
y					-6

7 Copy and complete the table of values for $2x - 3y = 18$ and draw its graph.

x	-3	0	3	6	9	12
y			-4			

8 Copy and complete the table of values for $y = -\frac{3}{4}x + 1$ and draw its graph.

x	-8	-4	0	4	8
y	7				

9 By finding the coordinates of three points on the line, draw each of the following lines between $x = -4$ and $x = 4$.

    (a) $y = 4x + 1$ (b) $y = -3x + 4$ (c) $y = \frac{1}{3}x + 2$

    (d) $y = 5 - \frac{1}{2}x$ (e) $x + y = 2$ (f) $2x + y = 4$

    (g) $x - y = 3$ (h) $3x + 2y = 6$ (i) $3x - 2y = 6$

10 For each line in question **9** write down the coordinates of the point where it crosses the y-axis.

How are your answers to (g) and (i) different from the others?

Mixed exercise 5

1 (a) Draw coordinate axes for x and y from -5 to $+5$.
Plot the following points.
$A(2, 3)$ $B(2, -4)$ $C(-1, 3)$ $D(-5, -3)$ $E(0, -4)$
$F(3, 0)$ $G(-2, -3)$ $H(5, -2)$

    (b) Work out the coordinates of the mid-points for the line segments BE, AG, AC, DG, EH, CD, GH and CE.

2 $A(1, 4)$, $B(2, 6)$ and $C(6, 3)$ are three points. Find the coordinates of the three possible points, D, which could complete a parallelogram.

3 $A(-2, 5)$ and $C(4, 3)$ are opposite vertices of a square. Find the coordinates of the other two vertices.

4 Here is a cube.

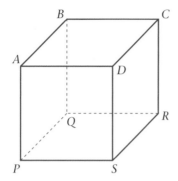

Say whether the shape made by the (lettered) points is 1-D, 2-D or 3-D.

(a) *AB*   (b) *ABC*   (c) *ABCD*   (d) *PR*

(e) *PABC*   (f) *PSB*   (g) *PQDA*   (h) *PQRSC*

(i) *PC*   (j) *PCR*

5 Copy and complete the table of values for $y = 4x + 5$ and draw its graph.

x	−3	−2	−1	0	1	2	3
y		−3					17

6 (a) Copy and complete the table of values for $y = 2x + 3$.

x	−2	−1	0	1	2	3
y		1	3			

(b) Draw the graph of $y = 2x + 3$.

(c) Use your graph to find
    (i) the value of y when $x = -1.3$
    (ii) the value of x when $y = 5.4$ [E]

> Use a grid for x from −2 to +3 and for y from −4 to +10.

7 Draw the graph of $y = 2x - 1$ for values of x from −2 to 3.

8 Draw the graph of $y = -3x + 5$ for values of x from −2 to 4.

9 Draw the graph of $x + y = 2$ for values of x from −2 to 4.

10 By finding the coordinates of three points on the line, draw the graph of $x + 2y = 4$ between $x = -2$ and $x = 6$.

11 By finding the coordinates of three points on the line, draw the graph of $5x + 2y = 10$ between $x = -2$ and $x = 4$.

Summary of key points

1 The x- and y-axes can both be extended to include negative numbers. Coordinates can include positive and negative numbers.

2 The x- and y-axes divide the coordinate grid into four **quadrants**.

3 The **mid-point** of the line segment joining (a, b) and (c, d) is
$$\left(\frac{a + c}{2}, \frac{b + d}{2}\right)$$

4 The number line goes in one direction.
It is **one-dimensional (1-D** for short).

5 The coordinates on a grid go in two directions. They cover a flat shape which is **two-dimensional (2-D** for short).

6 Solid shapes, space and volumes are **three-dimensional (3-D** for short). To describe positions in space, a third axis is used. This is the z-axis. 3-D coordinates look like this: (4, 5, 7).

7 Lines parallel to the x-axis have equations $y = $ a constant.

8 Lines parallel to the y-axis have equations $x = $ a constant.

9 The equation of the straight line passing through (0, 0), such that for each point on the line the x-coordinate equals the y-coordinate, is
$$y = x$$

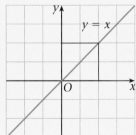

10 The equation of the straight line passing through (0, 0), such that for each point on the line the x-coordinate equals the negative of the y-coordinate, is
$$y = -x$$

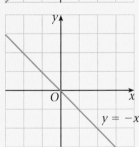

11 The equation of any straight line passing through (0, 0) is always either

y = a positive number times x ($y = ax$)

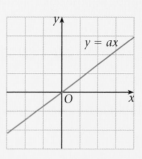

or

y = a negative number times x ($y = -ax$)

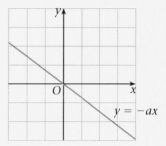

Remember $x = 0$ is the y-axis and $y = 0$ is the x-axis.
Both these lines pass through (0, 0).

12 Equations like $y = 2x + 2$, $y = -2x + 1$ and $y = \frac{1}{2}x - 5$ are equations of straight lines.

13 The coordinates of any point on a straight line satisfy its equation.

14 In general, $y = mx + c$ is the equation of a straight line. m may be positive or negative, a whole number or a fraction.

15 Equations like $x + y = 3$, $2x + 3y = 12$ and $3x - 5y = 15$ are also equations of straight lines, as they can be written in the form $y = mx + c$.

16 You only need two points on a line to be able to draw it, but a third point is a useful check.

6 Sequences

6.1 Term to term rules

- A **sequence** is a succession of numbers formed according to a rule.
- The numbers in a sequence are called the **terms** of the sequence.
- The **term to term rule** for a sequence tells you what to do to each term to obtain the next term in the sequence.

Example 1

The first term in a sequence is 1. The rule for the sequence is **add** 2.

(a) Find the next three terms in the sequence.

(b) Write down the mathematical name for the numbers in this sequence.

(a) second term = $1 + 2 = 3$
third term = $3 + 2 = 5$
fourth term = $5 + 2 = 7$
The next three terms are 3, 5, 7.

(b) This is the sequence of odd numbers.

Example 2

The first term in a sequence is 3. The rule for the sequence is **multiply by** 3.

(a) Find the next three terms in the sequence.

(b) Write down the mathematical name for the numbers in this sequence.

(a) second term = $3 \times 3 = 9$
third term = $9 \times 3 = 27$
fourth term = $27 \times 3 = 81$
The next three terms are 9, 27, 81.

(b) This is the sequence of powers of 3.

$9 = 3^2$
$27 = 3^3$
$81 = 3^4$

Example 3

The first term in a sequence is 5.
The rule for the sequence is **multiply by 2 then add 3**.
Find the next three terms in the sequence.

second term = $5 \times 2 + 3 = 13$
third term   = $13 \times 2 + 3 = 29$
fourth term = $29 \times 2 + 3 = 61$
The next three terms are 13, 29, 61.

- To find the rule for a sequence, it often helps to find the **differences** between consecutive terms.

Consecutive terms are next to each other.

Example 4

The first five terms of a sequence are 20, 17, 14, 11, 8.
(a) Find the rule for this sequence.
(b) Find the next two terms in the sequence.

(a) Sequence   20   17   14   11   8

    Differences -3 -3 -3 -3
    The rule is **subtract 3**.
(b) The next two terms are $8 - 3 = 5$
                             $5 - 3 = 2$

Example 5

The first five terms in a sequence are 2, 5, 14, 41, 122.
Find the sixth term.

Sequence   2   5   14   41   122

Differences $+3$ $+9$ $+27$ $+81$
Each difference is three times the previous difference. So the next difference is $3 \times 81 = 243$.
     sixth term = $122 + 243 = 365$

Exercise 6A

1 For each of these sequences
    (i) find the next three terms in the sequence
    (ii) write down the mathematical name for the numbers in the sequence.
        (a) first term = 2; rule is **add 2**
        (b) first term = 5; rule is **add 5**
        (c) first term = 2; rule is **multiply by 2**.

2 Find the next three terms in each of these sequences.

   (a) first term = 19; rule is **subtract 4**

   (b) first term = 125; rule is **divide by 5**

   (c) first term = 1; rule is **multiply by 4 then add 3**

   (d) first term = 7; rule is **subtract 5 then multiply by 4**

   (e) first term = 56; rule is **add 8 then divide by 2.**

3 For each of these sequences

   (i) find the term to term rule for the sequence

   (ii) find the next two terms in the sequence.

      (a) 7, 13, 19, 25, 31, ...   (b) 36, 29, 22, 15, ...

      (c) 2, 10, 50, 250, ...   (d) 64, 32, 16, 8, ...

4 For each of these sequences

   (i) find the next two terms in the sequence

   (ii) write down the mathematical name of the numbers in the sequence

      (a) 9, 18, 27, 36, 45, ...   (b) 10, 100, 1000, 10 000, ...

5 For each of these sequences

   (i) find the term to term rule for the sequence

   (ii) find the next two terms in the sequence.

      (a) 35, 29, 23, 17, 11, ...   (b) 10 000, 1000, 100, 10, ...

      (c) −13, −10, −7, −4, ...   (d) 64, 16, 4, 1, ...

6 Find the next term for each of these sequences.

   (a) 5, 7, 11, 17, 25, ...   (b) 5, 7, 11, 19, 35, ...

   (c) 8, 14, 23, 35, 50, ...   (d) 2, 22, 39, 53, 64, ...

7 These patterns of dots show the first five **square** numbers 1, 4, 9, 16, 25.

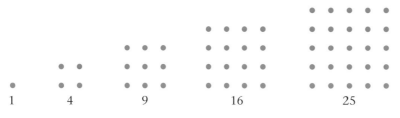

1   4   9   16   25

   (a) Find the differences for the first five square numbers.

   (b) Use your answer to (a) to write down a term to term rule for the sequence.

   (c) Use your rule to write down the next five square numbers.

8 These patterns of dots show the first five **triangle** numbers.

1   3   6   10   15

(a) Find the differences for the first five triangle numbers.

(b) Use your answer to (a) to write down a term to term rule for the sequence.

(c) Use your rule to write down the next five triangle numbers.

○ **12** Deriving formulae from sequences
12 Finding the rule and generating sequences

6.2 The nth term of a sequence

- You can use the **nth term** to generate any term in a sequence. Substitute the number of the term you want for n.

- A sequence where the differences between the terms are all the same (the same number is added or subtracted each time to obtain the next term) is called an **arithmetic sequence**.

For example, for the fourth term substitute $n = 4$.

Example 6

The nth term of a sequence is $5n - 2$. Find the first four terms.

Substituting $n = 1$, first term $= 5 \times 1 - 2 = 5 - 2 = 3$
Substituting $n = 2$, second term $= 5 \times 2 - 2 = 10 - 2 = 8$
Substituting $n = 3$, third term $= 5 \times 3 - 2 = 15 - 2 = 13$
Substituting $n = 4$, fourth term $= 5 \times 4 - 2 = 20 - 2 = 18$
The first four terms are 3, 8, 13, 18.

The differences are all 5, the same as the coefficient of n in the nth term.

- The general term for an arithmetic sequence is of the form $u_n = an + b$. The value of a is the difference between consecutive terms in the sequence.

Example 7

The first five terms of a sequence are 11, 7, 3, -1, -5.
Find an expression for the nth term of the sequence.

Sequence   11   7   3 -1 -5

Differences -4 -4 -4 -4

$-4n$ -4 -8 -12 -16 -20

$-4 + 15 = 11$ $-8 + 15 = 7$

The nth term is $15 - 4n$

The nth term contains $-4n$.

To obtain the required sequence, 15 must be added to each term.

Exercise 6B

1 For sequences with these nth terms, find
  (i) the first five terms in the sequence
  (ii) the twelfth term of the sequence.
     (a) $6n$ **(b)** $3n + 2$ **(c)** $7n - 3$
     (d) $32 - 5n$ **(e)** $24 - 8n$

2 Here are the first five terms of some sequences.
  Find an expression for the nth term of each of the sequences.
     (a) 7, 14, 21, 28, 35, ...   **(b)** 11, 17, 23, 29, 35, ...
     (c) 7, 8, 9, 10, 11, ...   **(d)** 23, 19, 15, 11, 7, ...
     (e) 5, 13, 21, 29, 37, ...   **(f)** 12, 11, 10, 9, 8, ...
     (g) 31, 21, 11, 1, −9, ...   **(h)** −14, −7, 0, 7, 14, ...

3 Find an expression for the nth term of each of these sequences.
     (a) even numbers starting with 2
     (b) odd numbers starting with 1
     (c) multiples of 8 starting with 8
     (d) even numbers starting with 10
     (e) odd numbers starting with 15
     (f) multiples of 5 starting with 35.

6.3 Sequences of shapes

Example 8

Here are the first four shapes in a sequence made from matchsticks.

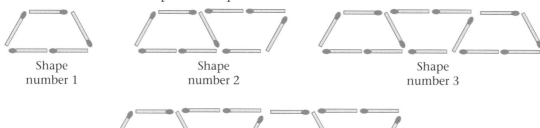

Shape number 1   Shape number 2   Shape number 3

Shape number 4

The table shows the number of matchsticks in each of these shapes.

Shape number (n)	1	2	3	4
Number of matchsticks	5	9	13	17

(a) Work out the number of matchsticks in shape number 5 and in shape number 6.
(b) Find an expression for the number of matchsticks in shape number n.
(c) Find the number of matchsticks in shape number 13.
(d) Find the shape number of the shape with 77 matchsticks.

In other words, find the nth term of the sequence 5, 9, 13, 17.

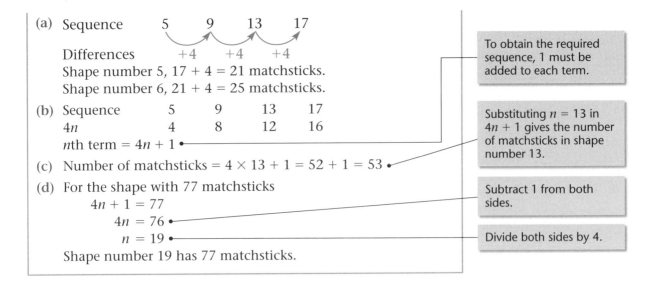

(a) Sequence   5   9   13   17

> To obtain the required sequence, 1 must be added to each term.

Differences   +4   +4   +4

Shape number 5, $17 + 4 = 21$ matchsticks.

Shape number 6, $21 + 4 = 25$ matchsticks.

(b) Sequence   5   9   13   17

$4n$ 4   8   12   16

nth term $= 4n + 1$

> Substituting $n = 13$ in $4n + 1$ gives the number of matchsticks in shape number 13.

(c) Number of matchsticks $= 4 \times 13 + 1 = 52 + 1 = 53$

(d) For the shape with 77 matchsticks

$$4n + 1 = 77$$
$$4n = 76$$
$$n = 19$$

> Subtract 1 from both sides.

> Divide both sides by 4.

Shape number 19 has 77 matchsticks.

Exercise 6C

1 Here are the first four shapes in four sequences of shapes made from matchsticks.

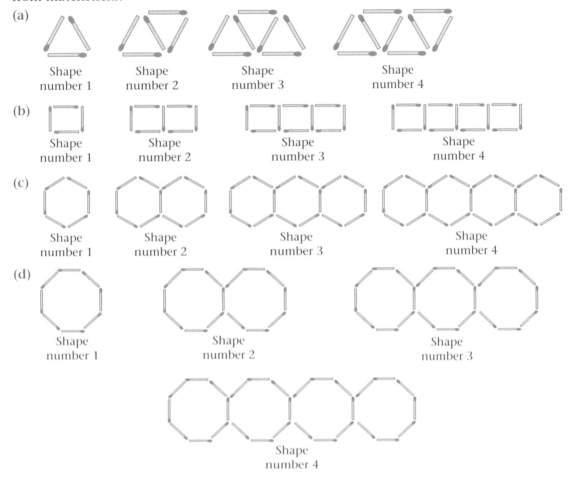

(a)

Shape number 1   Shape number 2   Shape number 3   Shape number 4

(b)

Shape number 1   Shape number 2   Shape number 3   Shape number 4

(c)

Shape number 1   Shape number 2   Shape number 3   Shape number 4

(d)

Shape number 1   Shape number 2   Shape number 3

Shape number 4

For each sequence
- (i) work out the number of matchsticks in shape number 5 and in shape number 6
- (ii) find an expression for the number of matchsticks in shape number n
- (iii) find the number of matchsticks in shape number 30
- (iv) find the number of the shape with 211 matchsticks.

2 (a) In question **1**, how is the coefficient of n in the expression for the number of matchsticks in shape number n related to the number of matchsticks in shape number 1? Explain why this is so.

(b) Write down an expression for the number of matchsticks in shape number n when the matchsticks in shape number 1 form a regular 20-sided polygon.

3 Here are four patterns made with square tiles.

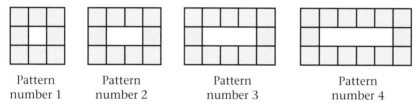

| Pattern number 1 | Pattern number 2 | Pattern number 3 | Pattern number 4 |

(a) Work out the number of tiles in pattern number 5 and in pattern number 6.

(b) Find an expression for the number of tiles in pattern number n.

(c) Find the number of tiles in pattern number 17.

(d) Find the pattern number of the pattern with 70 tiles.

4 Here are four patterns of dots.

| Pattern number 1 | Pattern number 2 | Pattern number 3 | Pattern number 4 |

(a) Work out the number of dots in pattern number 5 and in pattern number 6.

(b) Find an expression for the number of dots in pattern number n.

(c) Find the number of dots in pattern number 29.

(d) Find the pattern number of the pattern with 110 dots.

5   Here are four patterns made with square tiles.

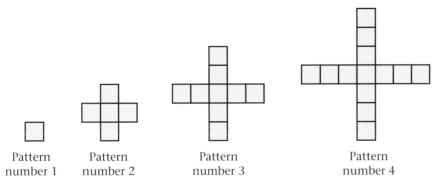

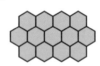

| Pattern | Pattern | Pattern | Pattern |
| number 1 | number 2 | number 3 | number 4 |

(a) Work out the number of tiles in pattern number 5 and in
     pattern number 6.

(b) Find an expression for the number of tiles in pattern
     number n.

(c) Find the number of tiles in pattern number 25.

(d) Find the pattern number of the pattern with 89 tiles.

(e) Find the pattern number of the largest pattern that can be
     made with 60 tiles.

6   Here are four patterns made with hexagonal tiles.

| Pattern | Pattern | Pattern | Pattern |
| number 1 | number 2 | number 3 | number 4 |

(a) Work out the number of tiles in pattern number 5 and in
     pattern number 6.

(b) Find an expression for the number of tiles in pattern
     number n.

(c) Find the number of tiles in pattern number 28.

(d) Find the pattern number of the pattern with 130 tiles.

(e) Find the pattern number of the largest pattern that can be
     made with 80 tiles.

Mixed exercise 6

1   Find the next three terms in each of these sequences. You are told
    the first term and the term to term rule.

(a) first term = 13; rule is **add 7**

(b) first term = 3; rule is **multiply by 4**

(c) first term = 5; rule is **multiply by 5 then subtract 1**

(d) first term = 11; rule is **subtract 5 then multiply by 2.**

2 Here are the first five terms of a number pattern.

    3   7   11   15   19

  (a) Write down the next term in the number pattern.

  (b) Work out the 8th term in the number pattern.   [E]

3 For each of these sequences

  (i) find the term to term rule for the sequence

  (ii) find the next two terms in the sequence.

      (a) 3, 11, 19, 27, 35, ...

      (b) 8, 4, 2, 1, $\frac{1}{2}$, ...

      (c) 20, 16, 12, 8, 4, ...

      (d) 3, 7, 15, 31, 63, ...

4 For each of these position to term rules, find

  (i) the first five terms in the sequence

  (ii) the tenth term of the sequence

  (iii) an expression for the nth term of the sequence.

> A **position to term rule** links the term number (or position) to the term.

      (a) multiply the term number by 7 and add 5

      (b) multiply the term number by 9 and subtract 8

      (c) multiply the term number by 5 and subtract from 20.

5 For sequences with these nth terms, find

  (i) the first five terms of the sequence

  (ii) the twentieth term of the sequence.

      (a) $9n - 7$ (b) $8n + 3$

      (c) $40 - 6n$ (d) $2 - 3n$

6 Here are the first five terms of some sequences.
Find an expression for the nth term of each of the sequences.

  (a) 3, 10, 17, 24, 31, ...   (b) 20, 17, 14, 11, 8, ...

  (c) 13, 21, 29, 37, 45, ...   (d) 5, 0, -5, -10, -15, ...

7 Here are the first five terms of a number sequence.

    3   8   13   18   23

  (a) Write down the next two terms of the sequence.

  (b) Explain how you found your answer.

  (c) Explain why 387 is not a term of the sequence.   [E]

8 The first five terms of an arithmetic sequence are

    4   11   18   25   32

  (a) Find, in terms of n, an expression for the nth term of the sequence.

  Jane says 697 is a term in the arithmetic sequence.

  (b) Is Jane correct? You must justify your answer.   [E]

9 Here are some patterns made up of dots.

Pattern number 1   Pattern number 2   Pattern number 3

(a) Draw pattern number 4.

(b) Copy and complete the table.

Pattern number	1	2	3	4	5
Number of dots	10	14	18		

(c) How many dots are used in pattern number 10?

(d) Write down a formula for the number of dots, d, in terms of the pattern number, n.

10 Here are the first four shapes in a sequence of shapes made from matchsticks.

 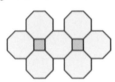 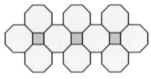 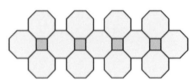

Shape   Shape   Shape   Shape
number 1   number 2   number 3   number 4

(a) Work out the number of matchsticks in shape number 5 and in shape number 6.

(b) Find an expression for the number of matchsticks in shape number n.

(c) Find the number of matchsticks in shape number 23.

(d) Find the shape number of the shape with 56 matchsticks.

(e) Find the shape number of the largest shape which can be made with 200 matchsticks.

11 Here are four patterns made with octagonal tiles and square tiles.

Pattern   Pattern   Pattern   Pattern
number 1   number 2   number 3   number 4

(a) Work out the **total** number of tiles in pattern number 5 and in pattern number 6.

(b) Find an expression for the number of **octagonal** tiles in pattern number n.

(c) Find an expression for the **total** number of tiles in pattern number n.

(d) Find the number of octagonal tiles in pattern number 12.

(e) Find the total number of tiles in pattern number 25.

(f) Find the number of octagonal tiles in a pattern with 13 square tiles.

(g) Find the total number of tiles in a pattern with 58 octagonal tiles.

Summary of key points

1 A **sequence** is a succession of numbers formed according to a rule.

2 The numbers in a sequence are called the **terms** of the sequence.

3 The **term to term rule** for a sequence tells you what to do to each term to obtain the next term in the sequence.

4 To find the rule for a sequence, it often helps to find the **differences** between consecutive terms.

> **Consecutive** terms are next to each other.

5 You can use the **nth term** to generate any term in a sequence. Substitute the number of the term you want for n.

> For example, for the fourth term substitute $n = 4$

6 A sequence where the differences between the terms are all the same (the same number is added or subtracted each time to obtain the next term) is called an **arithmetic sequence**.

7 The general term for an arithmetic sequence is of the form $u_n = an + b$. The value of a is the difference between consecutive terms in the sequence.

7 Properties of shapes

7.1 Polygons

- A **polygon** is a 2-D shape with any number of straight sides. The table shows the special names for polygons with different numbers of sides.

Number of sides	Name of polygon
3	triangle
4	quadrilateral
5	pentagon
6	hexagon
7	heptagon
8	octagon
9	nonagon
10	decagon

This floor tiling pattern contains both pentagons and heptagons.

- A polygon is **regular** if all its sides and all its angles are equal.
- The point where two sides meet is called a **vertex**.

A triangle has three vertices.

- The angle at a vertex is a measure of the turn between the two sides that meet there. Angles are usually measured in degrees.

This is the angle between the two sides.

The angle can be named
- by its vertex.
  For example

A

- by a letter inside the angle
  For example

a

- by the three point notation
  For example angle ABC

D

A

B C

Exercise 7A

Write down the names of these polygons.

1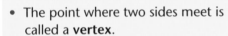

2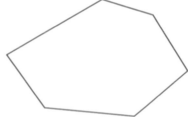

3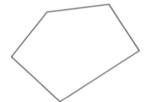

4

5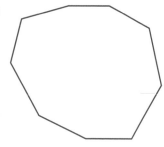

6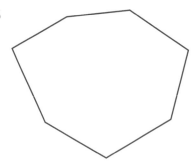

7.2 Properties of triangles

- A **triangle** is a polygon with three sides.

You need to recognise these special types of triangle.

Name	Shape	Properties
Scalene triangle		no sides equal no angles equal
Isosceles triangle		two sides equal two angles equal
Equilateral triangle		three sides equal three angles equal and 60°
Right-angled triangle		one angle 90°
Obtuse triangle		one angle greater than 90°
Acute triangle		all angles less than 90°

Scalene and isosceles triangles can be acute or obtuse. Equilateral triangles are always acute.

An **obtuse angle** is greater than 90° and less than 180°.

An **acute angle** is less than 90°.

Exercise 7B

Write down the names of these special types of triangle.
The first one is done for you.

1

right-angled triangle
scalene triangle

2

3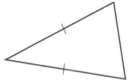

4

5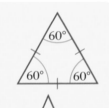

6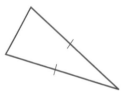

7

8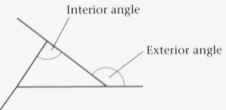

7.3 Angle properties of triangles

- In an equilateral triangle all angles are 60°.

- In an isosceles triangle two angles and two sides are equal.

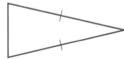

- The interior angles of a triangle always add up to 180°.

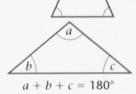

$a + b + c = 180°$

- If you extend each side of a triangle you get an exterior angle to the triangle.

Interior angle

Exterior angle

- The **exterior angle** of a triangle is equal to the sum of the interior angles at the other two vertices.

$c = a + b$

For a proof of this see Section 7.4.

Example 1

Work out the missing angles in these isosceles triangles.

(a)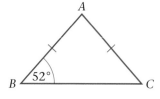

(b)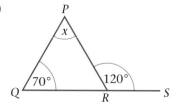

(a) angle $B = 52°$
     angle $C = 52°$

(b) $x + 70° = 120°$
     $x = 50°$

> Exterior angle = sum of
> interior opposite angles.

angle $A = 180° - 52° - 52°$
angle $A = 76°$

Example 2

Find the angles in this triangle.

Because the triangle is isosceles, the unmarked angle must be a.
So $a + a + 3a = 180°$
$5a = 180°$
$a = 36°$
The angles must be 36°, 36° and 108°.

Exercise 7C

In questions **1–10** work out the marked angles.

1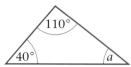

2

3

4

5

6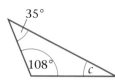

7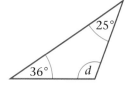

8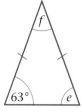

9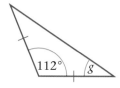

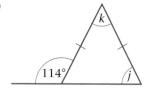

10

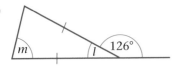

11 Work out the value of the letter:

   (a)

   (b)

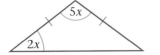

   (c)

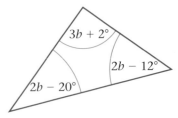

   (d)

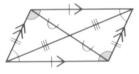

   (e)

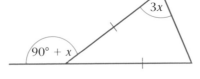

7.4 Properties of quadrilaterals

- A **quadrilateral** is a polygon with four sides.

You need to recognise these special types of quadrilateral.

Name	Shape	Properties
Trapezium		one pair of parallel sides
Parallelogram		two pairs of parallel sides opposite sides equal opposite angles equal diagonals bisect each other
Rhombus		two pairs of parallel sides opposite angles equal all sides equal diagonals bisect each other at right angles diagonals bisect the angles at the vertices
Rectangle		two pairs of parallel sides all angles are 90° opposite sides are equal diagonals are equal and bisect each other

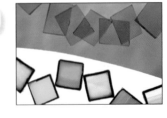

Square all sides equal
all angles 90°
opposite sides parallel
diagonals are equal and bisect
each other at right angles

Kite 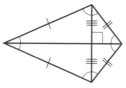 two pairs of adjacent sides equal
one pair of opposite angles equal
diagonals cross at right angles
one diagonal bisected by
the other diagonal

Arrowhead 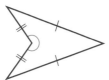 two pairs of adjacent sides
equal
one angle bigger than 180°

Exercise 7D

Write down the names of these special types of quadrilateral.

1    2   3

4 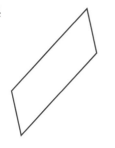   5 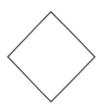   6

7    8    9

10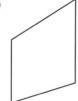

11 Write down the names of all quadrilaterals with
   (a)   all angles 90°
   (b)   opposite sides parallel
   (c)   one angle greater than 180°
   (d)   diagonals that bisect each other
   (e)   two pairs of adjacent sides equal.

12 Write down the names of the special quadrilaterals below and
show their properties on copies of the diagrams.

(a)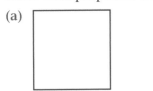

(b)

(c)

(d)

7.5 **Parallel lines, alternate and corresponding angles**

3 Angles on a straight line
3 Angles on a straight line (algebraic)
3 Testing the relations between angles

- Angles on a straight line add up to 180°.

$a + b = 180°$

- Vertically opposite angles are equal.

- A straight line crossing parallel lines creates **corresponding angles**. Corresponding angles are equal.

Sometimes called F angles

- A straight line crossing parallel lines creates **alternate angles**. Alternate angles are equal.

Sometimes called Z angles

Example 3

In the diagram, *ABE* is isosceles with *EA = EB*. Work out, giving your reasons, the size of the acute angle at *C*.

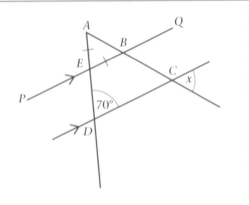

angle $AEB = 70°$ corresponding angles

angle EAB = angle EBA isosceles triangle

angle EAB + angle $EBA = 180° - 70° = 110°$ angles of a triangle add up to 180°

angle $EBA = 55°$

angle $QBC = 55°$ vertically opposite angles

$x = 55°$ corresponding angles

Exercise 7E

1 Give the size of a.
   Give a reason for your answer.

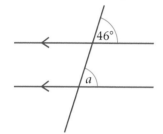

2 Give the size of b.
   Give a reason for your answer.

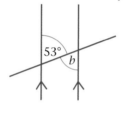

In questions **3–12** find the angle(s) marked with letters.
Give reasons for your answers.

3

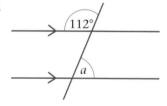

4

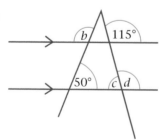

5

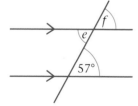

6

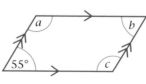

7

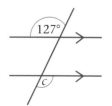

8

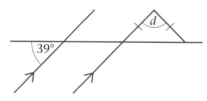

9

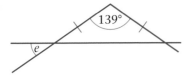

10

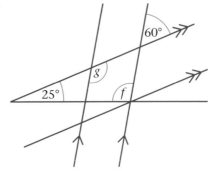

11

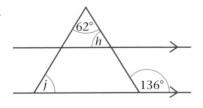

12

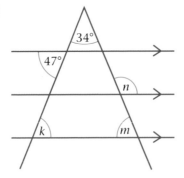

7.6 Proof in geometry

- In a **proof** you have to explain each step carefully and give reasons for your results.

You need to be able to prove that the exterior angle of a triangle is equal to the sum of the two interior and opposite angles.

Proof

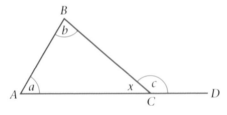

You have to prove that
$a + b = c$.

If the interior angle C of the triangle is called x then the exterior angle c is $180° - x$ ($180°$ in a straight line).
If the interior angle C of the triangle is called x then $a + b + x = 180°$ (angles in a triangle) and $a + b = 180° - x$.
So $c = 180° - x = a + b =$ the sum of the interior and opposite angles.

Exercise 7F

1 Prove that each angle of this equilateral triangle is 60°.

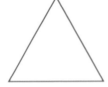

2 Prove that angle x is 40° in this isosceles triangle.

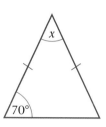

3 Prove that the three interior angles of a triangle add up to 180°.

4 Prove that angle $a = 80°$.

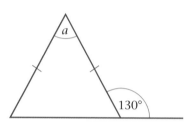

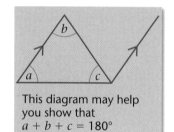

This diagram may help you show that
$a + b + c = 180°$

5 Prove that triangle *ABC* is isosceles.

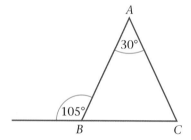

6 Prove that opposite angles in a parallelogram are equal.

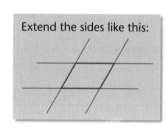

Extend the sides like this:

7.7 Bearings

Bearings are a means of indicating direction.

- Bearings are always measured from North.
- Bearings are always measured clockwise.
- They are written as three figures.

Add zeros in front of the number if necessary.

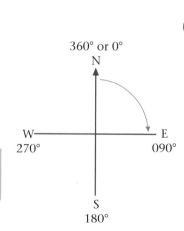

3 Angles around a point
3 Angles around a point (algebraic)

Example 4

A ship sails on a bearing of 060° from
a port *P*.
Draw a diagram to show this.

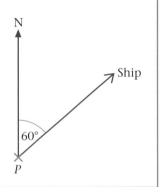

The angle measured from
North is 60°

Example 5

Sam walks on a bearing of 120° from his tent.
On what bearing must Sam walk to get back to his tent?

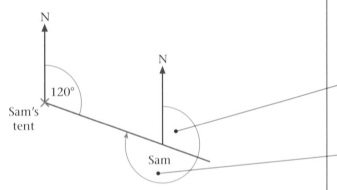

The North lines are
parallel.
This angle is 120°
(corresponding angles).

This angle is 180°
because it is a straight
line.

Sam must walk on a bearing of
    120° + 180° = 300°

Exercise 7G

1 Draw diagrams to show these bearings
   (a) 030°   (b) 150°   (c) 210°   (d) 300°

2 Write down the bearings of *A* from *P*.
   (a)   (b)   (c)

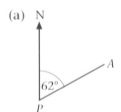

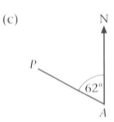

3 The bearing of *A* from *B* is 075°.
   Work out the bearing of *B* from *A*.

4 The bearing of P from Q is 245°.
Work out the bearing of Q from P.

5 The bearing of X from Y is b.
Investigate the relationship between the bearing of X from Y and
the bearing of Y from X when

(i) $0 < b < 180°$ (ii) $180° < b < 360°$

Mixed exercise 7

In questions **1–5** find the value of the letter.

1

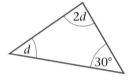

2

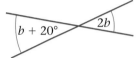

3

4

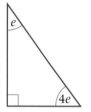

5

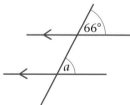

6 Work out $\angle ADB$.

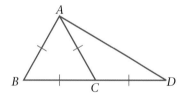

7 Give the size of a.
Give a reason for your answer.

8

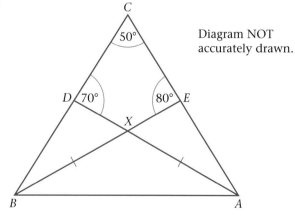

Diagram NOT
accurately drawn.

(a) Find $\angle XBA$.

(b) Explain why triangle CEB is isosceles.

9

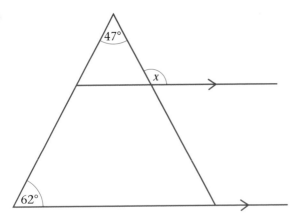

(a) Find angle x.

(b) Give reasons for your answer.

In questions **10–11** work out the size of the marked angle(s).
Give reason(s) for your answers.

10

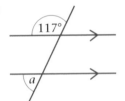

11

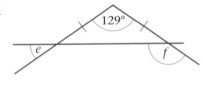

12

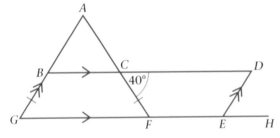

Prove △ABC is isosceles.
Hence find the size of angle BAC.

13 The diagram shows the position of
each of three buildings in a town.
The bearing of the hospital from
the art gallery is 072°.
The cinema is due East of the
hospital.
The distance from the hospital
to the art gallery is equal to the
distance from the hospital to the
cinema.

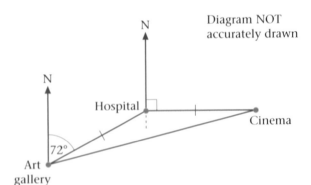

Diagram NOT
accurately drawn

Work out the bearing of the cinema from the art gallery. [E]

Summary of key points

1 A **polygon** is a 2-D shape with any number of straight sides.

2 A polygon is **regular** if all its sides and all its angles are equal.

3 The point where two sides meet is called a **vertex**.

The plural of 'vertex' is **'vertices'**.

4 The angle at a vertex is a measure of the turn between the two sides that meet there. Angles are usually measured in degrees.

5 A **triangle** is a polygon with three sides.

6 In an equilateral triangle all angles are 60°.

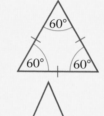

7 In an isosceles triangle two angles and two sides are equal.

8 The interior angles of a triangle always add up to 180°.

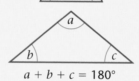

$a + b + c = 180°$

9 If you extend each side of a triangle you get an exterior angle to the triangle.

Interior angle

Exterior angle

10 The **exterior angle** of a triangle is equal to the sum of the interior angles at the other two vertices.

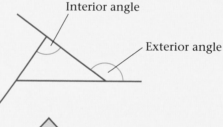

$c = a + b$

11 A **quadrilateral** is a polygon with four sides.

12 Angles on a straight line add up to 180°.

$a + b = 180°$

13 Vertically opposite angles are equal.

14 A straight line crossing parallel lines creates **corresponding angles**.
Corresponding angles are equal.

Sometimes called F angles

15 A straight line crossing
parallel lines creates
alternate angles.
Alternate angles are
equal.

Sometimes called
Z angles

16 In a **proof** you have to explain each step carefully and give reasons
for your results.

8 Properties of circles

8.1 Circle parts

22 Parts of a circle

- A **circle** is the shape enclosed by a curve which is everywhere the same distance from the centre.

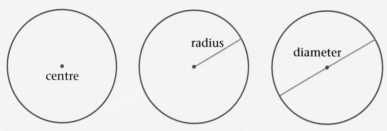

- The **circumference** of a circle is the distance measured around the curve which makes the circle.
- A **chord** is a straight line drawn across a circle.

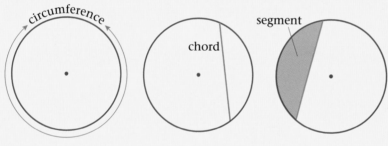

A segment is the
area lying between
a chord and an arc.

- A **tangent** to a circle touches the circle at one point only. The radius is at 90° to the tangent.

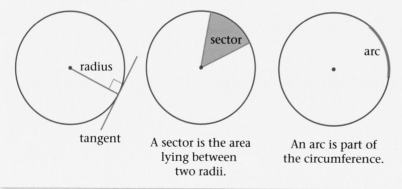

A sector is the area
lying between
two radii.

An arc is part of
the circumference.

Exercise 8A

1 Draw a diagram to show radius, diameter and circumference.

2 Draw a diagram to show arc, circumference and tangent.

3 Draw a diagram to show chord, sector and segment.

8.2 Tangents to circles

- A radius drawn from the point where a tangent touches a circle is perpendicular to the tangent.

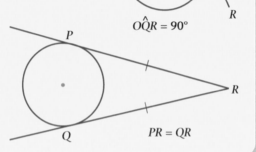

$$O\hat{Q}R = 90°$$

- Tangents drawn to a circle from a point outside the circle are equal in length.

$$PR = QR$$

Example 1

PR is a tangent to the circle and *MQ* is a diameter.

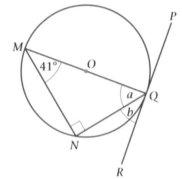

(a) Work out angle *a*.
(b) Work out angle *b*.
Give reasons for your answers.

(a) $a + 41° + 90° = 180°$ (sum of the angles in a triangle)
    so $a = 180° - 41° - 90°$
                    $a = 180° - 131°$
                    $a = 49°$

(b) $b + 49° = 90°$ (tangent perpendicular to radius)
    so $b = 90° - 49°$
                    $b = 41°$

Example 2

RP and RQ are tangents from R to the circle.

$R\hat{P}Q = 81°$

Calculate (a) $P\hat{R}Q$

  (b) $O\hat{P}Q$

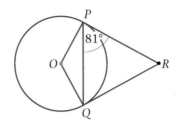

(a) RP and RQ are tangents from R, so triangle PQR is isosceles.

  So $R\hat{Q}P = R\hat{P}Q$

    $R\hat{Q}P = 81°$

  Then $P\hat{R}Q + 81° + 81° = 180°$ (sum of the angles of a triangle)

  so $P\hat{R}Q = 180° - 81° - 81°$

    $P\hat{R}Q = 180° - 162°$

    $P\hat{R}Q = 18°$

(b) $O\hat{P}Q + 81° = 90°$ (tangent perpendicular to radius)

  so $O\hat{P}Q = 90° - 81°$

    $O\hat{P}Q = 9°$

Exercise 8B

In all questions O is the centre of the circle.

1

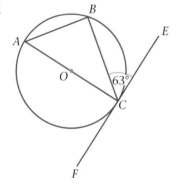

Diagram NOT accurately drawn

In the diagram, A, B and C are points on the circle, centre O.

Angle BCE = 63°.

FE is a tangent to the circle at point C.

Calculate the size of angle ACB.

Give reasons for your answer.   [E]

2 AB is a tangent to the circle, diameter CD.

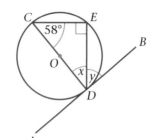

(a) Calculate the size of angle x.

(b) Calculate the size of angle y.

Give reasons for your answers.

3 TP and TQ are the tangents from T to the circle.

Angle PTQ = 42°.

Calculate the size of

(a) angle QPT

(b) angle OPQ.

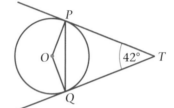

4 TA and TB are the tangents from T to the circle.

$T\hat{B}A = 67°$

Calculate (a) angle $A\hat{T}B$

(b) $O\hat{B}A$

giving reasons for your answers.

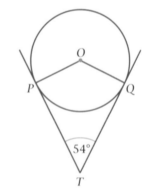

5 TP and TQ are the tangents from T to the circle.

Angle PTQ = 54°.

Work out the size of

(a) angle PQT

(b) angle OPQ.

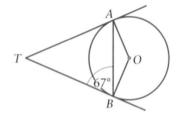

6 TM and TN are the tangents from T to the circle.

Angle MNT = 59°.

Work out the size of

(a) angle a

(b) angle b

giving reasons for your answers.

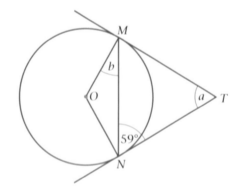

7 *AB* is a tangent to the circle.
DE is a diameter.
Angle *CDB* = 51°.
Calculate the size of

(a) angle *a*

(b) angle *b*

giving reasons for your answers.

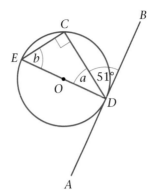

8.3 Drawing regular polygons

- The vertices of a regular polygon always lie on the circumference of a circle.

> In a regular polygon all sides and all angles are equal.

You can use this fact to construct regular polygons.

Example 3

Construct a regular octagon.

> An octagon has 8 sides, so divide the circumference of a circle into 8 equal arcs.
> For each arc the angle at the centre is $\frac{360}{8}$ = 45°.

> Join the points on the circumference.

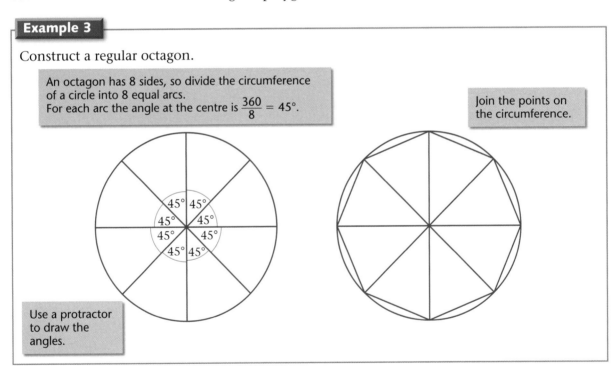

> Use a protractor to draw the angles.

Exercise 8C

1 Use the circle method to construct

(a) a regular hexagon

(b) a regular pentagon

(c) a regular nonagon (9 sides)

(d) a regular decagon (10 sides).

Summary of key points

1 A **circle** is the shape enclosed by a curve which is everywhere the same distance from the centre.

2 The **circumference** of a circle is the distance measured around the curve which makes the circle.

3 A **chord** is a straight line drawn across a circle.

4 A **tangent** to a circle touches the circle at one point only. The radius is at 90° to the tangent.

5 A radius drawn from the point where a tangent touches a circle is perpendicular to the tangent.

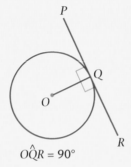

$O\hat{Q}R = 90°$

6 Tangents drawn to a circle from a point outside the circle are equal in length.

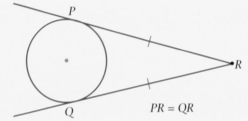

$PR = QR$

7 The vertices of a regular polygon always lie on the circumference of a circle.

9 Measures

9.1 Using suitable units

Any unit of length could be used to measure the distance between two telegraph poles:

$$0.06\,\text{km} \qquad 60\,\text{m} \qquad 6000\,\text{cm} \qquad 60\,000\,\text{mm}$$

All these represent the same distance, but in this case 60 m is the most sensible to use.

When working out areas and volumes the dimensions may be given in different units.

- Convert all measurements to the same units before you do a calculation.

Example 1

Wood weighs 700 kg per cubic metre.
Find the weight of a plank of wood measuring 2 m × 15 cm × 12 mm.

$15\,\text{cm} = 0.15\,\text{m}$
$12\,\text{mm} = 0.012\,\text{m}$
Volume $= 2 \times 0.15 \times 0.012 = 0.0036\,\text{m}^3$
Weight $= 0.0036 \times 700\,\text{kg} = 2.52\,\text{kg}$

> The weight is given per cubic metre, so change all measurements to metres.

Exercise 9A

1 A builder plans a concrete path measuring 20 metres long by 60 centimetres wide by 50 millimetres deep. What volume of concrete is needed for the path?

2 Paper weighs 80 grams per square metre. Work out the weight of a sheet of A4 paper. A4 measures 297 mm × 210 mm.

3 The radius of a wheel is 30 cm. How many revolutions does it make on a journey of 5 km?

> The circumference of a circle is $2\pi r$.

4 A telephone wire weighs 12.5 g per cubic centimetre. The radius of the wire is 1.2 mm. How much would 1 km of wire weigh?

5 How many litres of water are contained in a hosepipe with diameter 20 mm and length 30 metres?

6 Gold leaf comes in booklets of 10 sheets which measure 50 mm by 30 mm. How many booklets are required to cover 2 m²?

9.2 Metric and imperial equivalents

- You need to know these conversions.

Length	Weight	Capacity
10 mm = 1 cm 100 cm = 1 m 1000 mm = 1 m 1000 m = 1 km	1000 mg = 1 g 1000 g = 1 kg 1000 kg = 1 tonne (t)	100 c*l* = 1 litre 1000 m*l* = 1 litre 1000 *l* = 1 cubic metre

- You are expected to know these equivalents.
  - 1 kg = 2.2 pounds (lb)
  - 8 kilometres = 5 miles
  - 1 litre = 1.75 pints
  - 30 cm = 1 foot
  - 4.5 litres = 1 gallon

- These conversions may also be useful.
  - 25 g = 1 ounce (oz)
  - 1 m = 39 inches
  - 2.5 cm = 1 inch

Example 2

There are 640 acres in a square mile.
There are 100 hectares in a square kilometre.
How many acres are there in 1 hectare?

$1 \text{ hectare} = 10\,000 \text{ m}^2$

$$5 \text{ miles} = 8 \text{ kilometres}$$
So 25 square miles = 64 square kilometres
$$25 \times 640 \text{ acres} = 64 \times 100 \text{ hectares}$$
$$2.5 \text{ acres} = 1 \text{ hectare}$$

Exercise 9B

1 Change these weights.
  (a) 7 kg to pounds   (b) 600 g to pounds   (c) 3 lbs to kg
  (d) 96.5 lbs to kg   (e) 1 lb to kg

2 There are 14 lbs in a stone.
  Bill weighs 12 stone 10 lbs.
  What is his weight in kilograms?

3 Change 28 miles to kilometres.   [E]

4 Mary measures out 15 litres of water using a 1 pint milk bottle.
  How many full bottles would she need?

5 Petrol costs 98.4p per litre.
How much is this per gallon?

6 There are 16 ounces (oz) in a pound (lb).
A laptop computer weighs 7 lb 3 oz
How much does this laptop computer weigh in grams?

7 There are 12 inches in a foot.
Ajay is 5 feet 7 inches tall.
How tall is he in centimetres?

8 A fish tank measures 3 feet × 2 feet × 1 foot. How many litres of
water does it take to fill it?

> 1 litre = 1000 cm³

9 A petrol tank measures 35 cm × 24 cm × 60 cm. How many
gallons of petrol will it hold?

9.3 Accuracy

Measurements of time, length, weight, capacity and temperature are
continuous. They can never be measured exactly.

- If you make a measurement correct to a given unit the true value lies
  in a range that extends half a unit above and half a unit below that
  measurement.
- Measures expressed to a given unit have a possible error of half a unit.

Example 3

The length of a piece of string is 53 cm to the nearest cm.
(a) What is its minimum possible length?
(b) What is its maximum possible length?
(c) What is the maximum possible error?

(a) $53 - 0.5 = 52.5$ cm
(b) $53 + 0.5 = 53.5$ cm
(c) 0.5 cm

> 1 unit = 1 cm
> $\frac{1}{2}$ unit = 0.5 cm

Exercise 9C

In questions **1–4** all measurements are given correct to the nearest
unit. In each question, give the maximum and minimum possible
value for the exact measurement.

1 (a) 72 cm   (b) 16 mm   (c) 5 km   (d) 100 m

2 (a) 50 kg   (b) 125 g   (c) 3 tonnes   (d) 82 mg

3 (a) 4 h   (b) 23 minutes (c) 7 seconds   (d) 65 years

4 (a) 26 °C   (b) 55 °F   (c) 750 ml   (d) 8 litres

5 These measurements are to the nearest cm. Write down the maximum and minimum possible values.

  (a) 260 cm   (b) 5.28 m   (c) 600 mm   (d) 2000 mm

6 Write down the maximum error possible in an answer given to the nearest

  (a) hour   (b) 10 g   (c) 15 minutes
  (d) second   (e) 50 cm   (f) 0.2 seconds
  (g) 25 ml   (h) 5 °C.

9.4 Speed

- Speed = $\dfrac{\text{distance}}{\text{time}}$
- Average speed = $\dfrac{\text{total distance}}{\text{total time}}$

You can use this triangle to help you remember the formulae.

Cover the value you wish to find with your thumb: e.g. to find speed cover S. You are left with D over T, that is $\dfrac{\text{distance}}{\text{time}}$

Common units for speed are m/s (metres per second)
                        km/h (kilometres per hour)
                        mph (miles per hour).

Example 4

The average speed for a journey of 273 km was 57.2 km/h.

How long did the journey take?

Speed   = $\dfrac{\text{distance}}{\text{time}}$, so

Time   = $\dfrac{\text{distance}}{\text{speed}}$

Time   = $\dfrac{273}{57.2}$ = 4.772 727 3 hours

0.772 727 3 hours = 0.772 727 3 × 60 = 46 minutes

                        (to the nearest minute)

So the journey took 4 hours 46 minutes.

> The distance is in km, the speed is in km/h, so time is in hours.

> 1 hour = 60 minutes
> So 0.772 727 3 hours = 0.772 727 3 × 60 minutes.

Example 5

Ben travels 7.3 km in 8.5 minutes.

What is his average speed?

Give your answer in (a) metres per second and (b) kilometres per hour.

(a) average speed $= \dfrac{\text{distance}}{\text{time}}$

So speed $= \dfrac{7.3 \, \text{km}}{8.5 \, \text{minutes}}$

7.3 km $= 7300 \, \text{m}$ 8.5 minutes $= 510$ seconds

speed $= \dfrac{7300 \, \text{m}}{510 \, \text{seconds}}$

$= 14.3 \, \text{m/s}$ (1 d.p.)

> For an answer in metres per second change the units to metres and seconds.

(b) 8.5 minutes $= \dfrac{8.5}{60} = 0.141\dot{6}$ hours

Speed $= \dfrac{7.3 \, \text{km}}{0.141\dot{6} \, \text{hours}}$

$= 51.5 \, \text{km/h}$ (1 d.p.)

> For an answer in km/h change the minutes to hours.

Exercise 9D

1 Copy and complete the table.

	Distance	Time	Average speed
(a)	128 km	2 h	
(b)	58 miles		8 mph
(c)		20 s	30 m/s
(d)	2.3 km	50 s	
(e)		$3\frac{1}{2}$ h	50 mph
(f)	165 km	$2\frac{1}{2}$ h	
(g)	750 m		25 m/s
(h)		$2\frac{1}{2}$ min	40 m/s
(i)	100 km	50 min	
(j)	254 miles	1 h 15 min	
(k)	76 km		15 km/h
(l)	27.15 km	16 min 10 s	
(m)	127 miles		55 mph
(n)		3 h 18 min	30 mph
(o)	2350 km	$1\frac{1}{2}$ days	

2 A car travels for four hours at an average speed of 52 mph. How far does it travel?

3 According to the railway timetable the distance between London and Stoke on Trent is 148 miles and the journey takes 1 hour 36 minutes. What is the average speed for this journey?

4 The winner of a 100 m race took 9.3 seconds. What was his average speed?

5 How long does it take to do a journey of 190 kilometres at 55 km/h?

6 A sailing dinghy averages 3.5 m/s for 6 minutes. How far does it travel?

7 How far would you travel in 18 minutes at an average speed of 37 km/h?

8 How long does it take to travel 185 km at 40 km/h?

9 How long does it take to travel the 335 miles from London to Cornwall at an average speed of 37 mph?

10 A 308 km Grand Prix is completed in 1 hour and 25 minutes by the winner. What was the winner's average speed?

11 Myfanwy drives the 150 km from her home to Carnforth in 3 hours. Work out her average speed.

12 Errol cycles for $2\frac{1}{2}$ hours at an average speed of 18 km/h. How far does he travel?

13 The distance from London to Chicago is 6360 km. The flight takes 8 hours 15 minutes. What is the average speed of the aeroplane?

14 The speed of a shell fired from a gun is 1800 m s^{-1}. How far does it travel in 1 minute?

15 A Formula 1 racing car completes a 6.3 km lap in 1 minute 16.2 seconds. Work out the average speed in

(a) m s^{-1}

(b) km per hour.

16 The time gap between the first and second cars in a Grand Prix was 3.146 seconds. Assuming the cars were travelling at 305 km/h at the finish, work out how far apart they were.

9.5 Density

- Density = $\dfrac{\text{mass}}{\text{volume}}$

Common units for density are g/cm³ (g per cm³), kg/m³ (kg per m³).

You can use this triangle to help you remember the formulae.

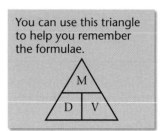

Example 6

The density of wood is 0.8 g per cubic centimetre. What is the mass of a post measuring 1.8 m by 75 mm by 75 mm?

1.8 m = 180 cm   75 mm = 7.5 cm
Volume = 180 × 7.5 × 7.5 = 10 125 cm³

Density = $\dfrac{\text{mass}}{\text{volume}}$, so mass = density × volume

Mass = 0.8 × 10 125 = 8100 g
　　 = 8.1 kg

Volume of cuboid = length × width × height

Density is in g/cm³ so convert measurements to cm.

Exercise 9E

1 The density of gold is 19.32 g per cm³. A gold bar has a mass of 12.5 kg. What is its volume?

2 A brick measures 230 mm by 110 mm by 70 mm. It has a mass of 3.2 kg. What is the density of the brick?

3 A decorative lamp is to be filled with glycerine. Its volume is 72 cm³ and the density of the glycerine is 1.27 g per cm³. What mass of glycerine is required?

4 Copy and complete the table.

Substance	Mass	Volume	Density
Hydrogen		1 km³	0.0009 g/cm³
Air	20 kg		0.0013 g/cm³
Copper	14.7 kg	164 cm³	

5 The density of silver is 10.5 g/cm³. To check whether a dish is solid silver it is weighed and its volume found by immersing the dish in water and measuring the water displaced. The volume is 52.3 cm³ and its mass is 611 g. Is the dish likely to be solid silver?

6 A ring is made from gold with a diamond. The ring has volume 0.95 cm³. The gold is known to have a mass of 15 g. The density of the gold is 19.3 g/cm³. Work out the volume of the diamond.

9.6 Changing units

- Compound measures combine measurements of two or more different types. For example, a speed is a measurement of a **distance** and the **time** taken to travel it.

You need to be able to change compound measures into different units.

Example 7

Change 20 metres per second to kilometres per hour.

In 1 second the distance travelled is 20 m

so in 1 hour the distance travelled is $20 \times 3600 = 72\,000$ m

In 1 hour distance travelled $= \dfrac{72\,000}{1000} = 72$ km

20 m/s $= 72$ km/h

There are $60 \times 60 = 3600$ seconds in an hour.

First work out how many metres will be travelled in 1 hour.

1000 m $= 1$ km

Example 8

Change 30 miles per hour to metres per second.
Use 5 miles = 8 kilometres

5 miles $= 8$ km
1 mile $= \frac{8}{5}$ km
30 miles $= 30 \times \frac{8}{5} = 48$ km

48 km $= 48\,000$ m

In 1 hour 48 000 m is travelled

So in 1 second $\dfrac{48\,000}{3600} = \dfrac{40}{3} = 13\frac{1}{3}$ m is travelled.

30 mph $= 13\frac{1}{3}$ m/s

Change miles to km.

Change km to m.

1 hour $= 60 \times 60 = 3600$ seconds.

Exercise 9F

1 Change 30 metres per second to kilometres per hour.

2 Change 96 km/h to metres per second.

3 Change 120 miles per hour to miles per minute.

4 Change 48 kilometres per hour to miles per hour.

5 Change 150 miles per hour to kilometres per hour.

6 An electron travels at 600 000 metres per second. What is this speed in miles per hour?

7 Change 120 miles per hour into metres per second.

8 Change 40 miles per gallon to kilometres per litre.

9 Change 40 kilometres per litre to miles per gallon.

10 Change £4.95 per pound (lb) to pence per kilogram.

11 Change 5 miles per gallon to kilometres per litre.

12 Change 3.7 kg per cubic metre to pounds (lb) per cubic foot.

13 A gallon of fertiliser covers 200 square feet. How many square metres are covered by 1 litre?

14 A pipe delivers 20 litres of oil per second. What is this in gallons per hour?

15 A pump removes 280 gallons of water in 5 minutes. What is the rate in litres per second?

9.7 Using estimates

- Sometimes you do not need an exact answer. You can round numbers to 1 significant figure and calculate an estimate.

Example 9

A cow needs 0.018 hectares of pasture.
A field measures 61.3 metres by 42.3 metres.
Roughly how many cows can it support?

Area of field = $61.3 \times 42.3 \, \text{m}^2$
1 hectare is $100 \times 100 \, \text{m}^2$, so $0.018 \, \text{ha} = 0.018 \times 100 \times 100 = 180 \, \text{m}^2$

Maximum number of cows = $\dfrac{61.3 \times 42.3}{180}$

An estimate is $\dfrac{60 \times 40}{200} = 12$

There is enough space for about 12 cows.

Change all units to metres.

Exercise 9G

Use estimates to answer these questions.

1 1 kg of seed is enough to sow about $30 \, \text{m}^2$. How much seed is required to sow 25 hectares?

2 The recommended concentration to mix a fertiliser is 17.6 g of fertiliser per litre of water. How much fertiliser is needed to mix 50 gallons?

3 A wall is 15 m long and 2 m high. It is built to a thickness of two bricks. The face of each brick measures 21 cm by 6 cm. How many bricks are needed?

4 The grain yield at a farm is known to be about 3.7 tonnes per hectare. What is the yield from a rectangular field measuring 143 metres by 208 metres?

9.8 Comparing measurements

- To compare prices for different sized packs, work out the price of a unit quantity in each.

> A **unit quantity** could be e.g. 1 g, 100 g, 1 kg.

Example 10

Which is the better buy?
A 1 kilogram tin costing £3.25 or a 450 gram packet costing £1.44?

In the tin, 1000 grams cost £3.25
100 grams cost 32.5p
In the packet, 450 grams cost £1.44
50 grams cost £1.44 ÷ 9 = 16p
100 grams cost 32p
The 450 gram packet is the better buy.

> Compare prices for 100 g in each pack.

- Measurements can be compared easily if they have the same units.

Example 11

A piece of coal weighs 3 kg and its volume is 1950 cm³.
4 cubic metres of sand weighs 6500 kg.
Which has the greater density – sand or coal?

$$\text{Density} = \frac{\text{mass}}{\text{volume}}$$

Density of sand $= \dfrac{6500}{4} = 1625 \text{ kg/m}^3$

Volume of coal $= 1950 \text{ cm}^3 = 1950 \div 1\,000\,000 \text{ m}^3 = 0.001\,950 \text{ m}^3$

Density of coal $= \dfrac{3}{0.001\,950} = 1538.46\ldots = 1538.5 \text{ kg/m}^3$

Sand has a greater density than coal.

> Change to m³
> $1 \text{ m}^3 = 10^6 \text{ cm}^3$

Exercise 9H

1 Car A is travelling at 65 mph.
Car B is travelling at 105 km per hour.
Which car is travelling the faster?

2 Which is the better buy, three for £1.19 or five for £1.99?

3 Which is best value?
A 330 m*l* can costing 45p or a 1 litre bottle costing £1.35?
Give a reason.

4 A small 50 g jar of coffee costs £1.35
A medium 100 g jar of coffee costs £2.75
A large 200 g jar of coffee costs £5.30
Find the cost per 100 g to decide which is the best buy.

5 The oil in a can has a volume of 5000 cm³ and mass 4 kg.
The water in a jug has a volume of 1500 cm³ and mass 1.5 kg.
Which has the greater density?

> You must show your working.

6 A block of gold has volume 3000 cm³ and mass 57 900 g.
A block of platinum has volume 2500 cm³ and mass 53 500 g.
Which has the greater density?

> You must show all your working.

7 James travels the 40 miles from London to Wycombe in $1\frac{1}{4}$ hours.
Nitin travels the 15 km from Whitechapel to Wanstead in
18 minutes.
Who had the faster average speed?

8 Petrol is priced at a garage at £4.20 per gallon or 95p per litre.
Which price is the better buy?

9 A swift flies at 50 metres per second.
An InterCity train travels at 120 miles per hour.
(a) Which travels the faster?
(b) What is the distance between them after 10 minutes?

> Assume they both start at the same point at the same time and travel in the same direction.

Mixed exercise 9

1 The distance between London and Exeter is 170 miles.
How far is this in kilometres?

2 A car's petrol tank can hold 25 gallons.
How many litres is this?

3 Work out the mass, in kilograms, of a 56 lb sack of potatoes.

4 A running track is 400 metres to the nearest metre.
Write down the greatest and least distance it could be.

5 How long does it take to travel 160 km at 50 km/h?

6 A runner sprints 400 metres in 48 seconds.
What is her speed in metres per second?

7 A cyclist plans to cycle non-stop the 870 miles from Land's End
to John O'Groats in six days. Work out the average speed.

> The cyclist travels for 12 hours per day.

8 A doorstop in the shape of a cuboid measuring 10 cm × 3 cm ×
5 cm is made from plastic with a density of 3.1 g/cm³. Work out
its mass.

9 A glass paperweight weighs 236 grams.
The density of the glass is 2.7 g/cm³.
Work out the volume of the paperweight.

10 The mass of 5 m³ of copper is 44 800 kg.

(a) Work out the density of copper.

The density of zinc is 7130 kg/m³.

(b) Work out the mass of 5 m³ of zinc. [E]

11 Change 230 centimetres per second into miles per hour.

12 Change 76 miles per hour into metres per second.

13 A 1 kg box of washing powder costs £6.50
A 3.5 kg tub of washing powder costs £23.00
Which is the better buy?

14 A horse rider and a car driver have a race.
The horse rider has a shorter journey through a forest.
The horse rider completes her 7.2 kilometre journey at an average
speed of 30 miles per hour. The car driver completes his 6 mile
journey at an average speed of 16 metres per second.

(a) Who wins?

(b) What is the difference in their times?

15 Brian walks at a speed of 2.2 metres per second.
Susan walks at a speed of 7 kilometres per hour.
Who walks quickest?

> You must show all your working.

16

These two metal blocks each have a volume of 0.5 m³.
The density of the copper block is 8900 kg per m³.
The density of the nickel block is 8800 kg per m³.

Calculate the difference in the masses of the blocks. [E]

Summary of key points

1 Convert all measurements to the same units before you do a calculation.

2 You need to know these conversions.

Length	Weight	Capacity
10 mm = 1 cm		
100 cm = 1 m		100 cl = 1 litre
1000 mm = 1 m	1000 mg = 1 g	1000 ml = 1 litre
1000 m = 1 km	1000 g = 1 kg	1000 l = 1 cubic metre
	1000 kg = 1 tonne (t)	

3 You are expected to know these equivalents.
   1 kg = 2.2 pounds (lb)
   8 kilometres = 5 miles
   1 litre = 1.75 pints
   30 cm = 1 foot
   4.5 litres = 1 gallon

4 These conversions may also be useful.
   25 g = 1 ounce (oz)
   1 m = 39 inches
   2.5 cm = 1 inch

5 If you make a measurement correct to a given unit the true value lies in a range that extends half a unit above and half a unit below that measurement.

6 Measures expressed to a given unit have a possible error of half a unit.

7 Speed = $\dfrac{\text{distance}}{\text{time}}$

8 Average speed = $\dfrac{\text{total distance}}{\text{total time}}$

9 Density = $\dfrac{\text{mass}}{\text{volume}}$

10 Compound measures combine measurements of two or more different types. For example, a speed is a measurement of a **distance** and the **time** taken to travel it.

11 Sometimes you do not need an exact answer. You can round numbers to 1 significant figure and calculate an estimate.

12 To compare prices for different sized packs, work out the price of a unit quantity in each.

> A **unit quantity** could be e.g. 1 g, 100 g, 1 kg.

13 Measurements can be compared easily if they have the same units.

10 Perimeter, area and volume

10.1 Area of plane shapes

- The area of a triangle is $\frac{1}{2}$ base $\times$ perpendicular height or $\frac{1}{2}bh$.

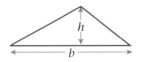

- The area of a parallelogram is base $\times$ perpendicular height or bh.

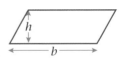

- The area of a trapezium is $\frac{1}{2}h(a + b)$ where a and b are the lengths of the parallel sides and h is the distance between the parallel sides.

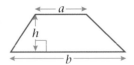

Example 1

Find the area of triangle ABC.

Area $= \frac{1}{2} \times 5 \times 8 = 20\,\text{cm}^2$

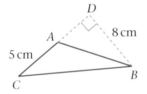

Any side of the triangle can be the base. Choose AC as the base. Then BD becomes the height.

Example 2

Find the area of this parallelogram.

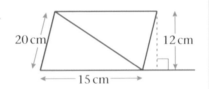

Area of parallelogram $= bh$
$$= 15 \times 12 = 180\,\text{cm}^2$$

Exercise 10A

1 $ABCD$ is a rectangle with area $296\,\text{cm}^2$. The length AB is $80\,\text{mm}$. Work out the height BC.

2 Work out the area of each parallelogram.

(a)

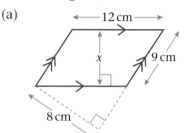

(b)

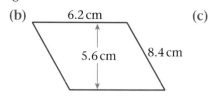

(c)

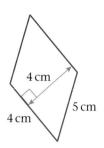

3 In each diagram, work out the value of *x*.

(a)

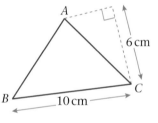

(b)

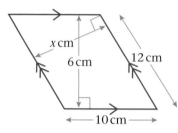

(c)

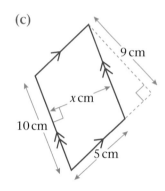

4 Work out the area of the triangles shown.

(a)

(b)

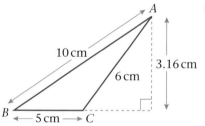

(c)

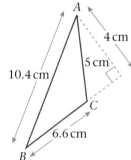

(d)

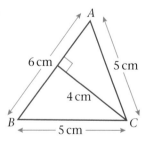

(e)

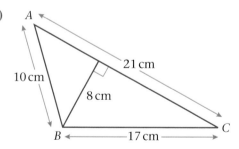

5 Find the area of each trapezium.

(a)

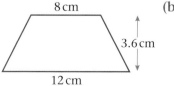

(b)

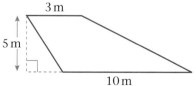

(c)

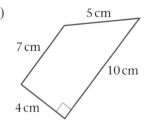

10.2 Surface area and volume of cuboids

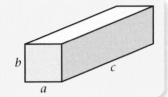 **13** Volume of cuboids

- Cuboid: surface area = $2(ab + bc + ac)$
  volume = abc

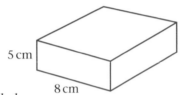

For more on surface area
see Section 10.4

Example 3

Find the total surface area of this
cuboid.
The end face measures 8 cm × 5 cm
and the volume is 480 cm³.

5 cm

8 cm

v = length × width × height = lwh
480 = 5 × 8 × length
length = 12 cm
Front face area = 8 × 5 = 40 cm²
Side face area = 5 × 12 = 60 cm²
Top face area   = 8 × 12 = 96 cm²
As there are two of each, the total surface area = 2(40 + 60 + 96)
                                                = 392 cm²

Exercise 10B

In questions **1–6**, find the volume of the cuboid. Give your answer to
a sensible degree of accuracy.

1 A storage box which measures 15 cm by 25 cm by 30 cm.

2 A fish tank which measures 42.2 cm by 20.8 cm by 17.3 cm.

3 A petrol tank which measures 83.1 cm by 45.1 cm by 23.9 cm.

4 A swimming pool which measures 6.32 m by 24.91 m by 1.64 m.

5 A stack of 500 sheets of paper. Each sheet measures 29.7 cm by
   21 cm and is 0.1 mm thick.

6 A chopping board which measures 25 cm by 35 cm by 6 mm.

7 Copy and complete the table for cuboids of different dimensions.

	Length	Width	Height	Volume
(a)	4 cm	5 cm		80 cm³
(b)	12 cm		3 cm	216 cm³
(c)	1.6 m	10 cm		6400 cm³
(d)	15 cm		20 mm	15 cm³
(e)		15 cm	2.2 m	1.32 m³
(f)		2.5 cm	6 mm	10.5 cm³
(g)		15 mm	5 cm	0.0018 m³
(h)	3 m	75 mm		6750 cm³

8 The surface area of a cube is 96 cm².
What is the length of an edge?

9 Work out the surface area of this cuboid.

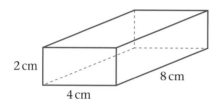

2 cm 4 cm 8 cm

10 The sum of the three different edges of a cuboid is 15 cm.
Copy and complete this table of possible volumes and surface areas.
Four have been done for you.

Size	1, 1, 13	1, 2, 12	2, 2, 11	1, 3, 11				
Volume	13	24	44	33				
Area	54	76	96	94				

What are the dimensions of

(a) the cuboid with the maximum volume

(b) the cuboid with the maximum surface area?

10.3 Fitting boxes into larger boxes

Example 4

The diagram shows a box measuring 30 cm × 50 cm × 20 cm which
is to be filled with packets measuring 5 cm × 4 cm × 10 cm.
How many packets are needed to completely fill the box?

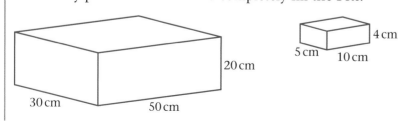

30 cm 50 cm 20 cm 5 cm 10 cm 4 cm

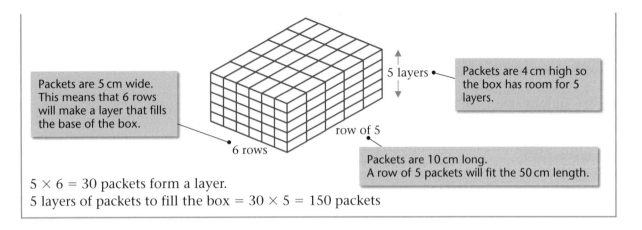

Packets are 5 cm wide. This means that 6 rows will make a layer that fills the base of the box.

5 layers

Packets are 4 cm high so the box has room for 5 layers.

row of 5

6 rows

Packets are 10 cm long. A row of 5 packets will fit the 50 cm length.

$5 \times 6 = 30$ packets form a layer.
5 layers of packets to fill the box $= 30 \times 5 = 150$ packets

Exercise 10C

1 Work out how many boxes measuring 2 cm × 3 cm × 5 cm will fit into a container measuring 20 cm × 30 cm × 50 cm.

2 Work out how many matchboxes measuring 1.5 cm × 4 cm × 6 cm exactly fill a packet measuring 15 cm × 20 cm × 30 cm.

3 Work out how many cereal packets measuring 9 cm × 20 cm × 32 cm will fill a container measuring 36 cm × 96 cm × 1 m.

4 The diagrams show a packet and a box. Find out how many packets will completely fill the box. The packet shown may not be facing the best way.

(a)　　　　　　　　(b)　　　　　　　　(c)

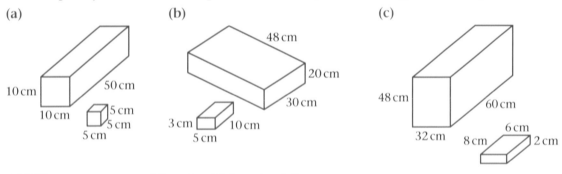

5 A DVD cover measures 19 cm by 13.5 cm by 1.5 cm.
How many DVDs will fit into a carton which measures 19 cm by 40.5 cm by 45 cm?

6 A mobile phone is packed in a box which measures 15 cm by 21 cm by 6 cm.
How many boxed mobile phones can be packed into a carton which measures 75 cm by 42 cm by 60 cm?

7 A box of matches measures 5 cm by $3\frac{1}{2}$ cm by $1\frac{1}{2}$ cm.
How many boxes of matches can be packed into a container which measures 25 cm by 3.5 cm by 15 cm?

Hint: a row of 5 matchboxes is 25 cm long.

8 Metric bricks are 20 cm long by 10 cm high.
How many bricks are required to build a wall 6 m long and 1.2 m high?

10.4 Surface area of simple shapes

- The **surface area** is the total araea of all the faces of a solid shape.

Example 5

Work out the total surface area of the prism in the diagram.

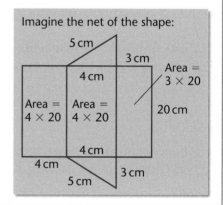

$$\text{Area of a triangular face} = \tfrac{1}{2} \times 3 \times 4 = 6\,\text{cm}^2$$
Area of the rectangular faces $= (3 \times 20)$, (5×20) and (4×20)
Total area of the rectangular faces $= 60 + 100 + 80 = 240\,\text{cm}^2$

Total surface area $= 6 + 6 + 240 = 252\,\text{cm}^2$

2 ends   3 rectangles

Imagine the net of the shape:

Exercise 10D

In each question work out the total surface area.

1 A 3 cm cube

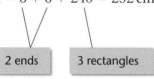

3 cm

2

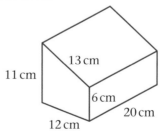

13 cm

11 cm

6 cm

20 cm

12 cm

3

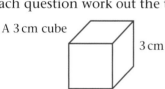

3 cm

3 cm

6 cm

8 cm

6 cm

4

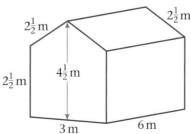

$2\tfrac{1}{2}$ m

$2\tfrac{1}{2}$ m

$4\tfrac{1}{2}$ m

$2\tfrac{1}{2}$ m

3 m

6 m

5

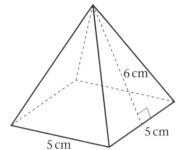

6

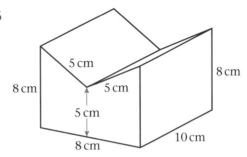

10.5 Volume of prisms

13 Volume of prisms

- A **prism** is a 3-D shape with the same cross-section all along its length.
- Volume of a prism = area of cross-section × length.

Example 6

Find the volume of the length of gutter shown.

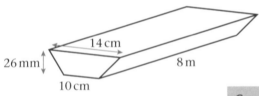

> Convert all measurements to the same unit, cm.

$26\,mm = 2.6\,cm$, $8\,m = 800\,cm$

Area of cross-section = $\frac{1}{2}(14 + 10) \times 2.6$

> Area of trapezium
> = $\frac{1}{2}(a + b)h$

Volume = $800 \times \frac{1}{2}(14 + 10) \times 2.6$

= $24\,960\,cm^3$

Exercise 10E

1 Work out the volumes of these wedges.

(a)

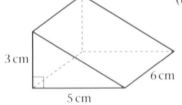

(b)

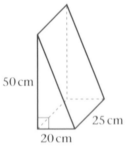

2   Work out **(i)** the volumes **(ii)** the total surface areas of these prisms.

(a)

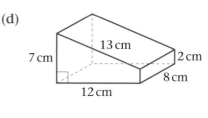

6 cm
15 cm
6 cm

(b)

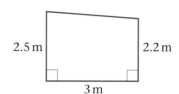

2.8 cm
8.5 cm
15 cm

(c)

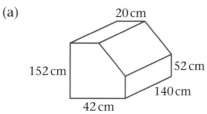

9 cm
15 cm
10 cm
12 cm

(d)

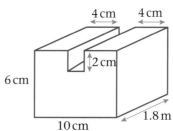

13 cm
7 cm
2 cm
8 cm
12 cm

3   The cross-section of Teo's bedroom is shown.
    The bedroom is 2.8 m long.
    Calculate the volume of Teo's bedroom.

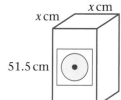

2.5 m   2.2 m
        3 m

4   A square loudspeaker is 51.5 cm tall.
    The volume of the loudspeaker is 34 814 cm³.
    Calculate the length of the square side of the loudspeaker.

x cm
x cm
51.5 cm

5   Work out the volumes of these prisms.

(a)

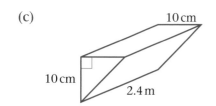

20 cm
152 cm
52 cm
140 cm
42 cm

(b)

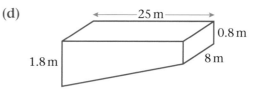

4 cm   4 cm
2 cm
6 cm
10 cm
1.8 m

(c)

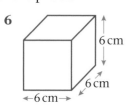

10 cm
10 cm
2.4 m

(d)

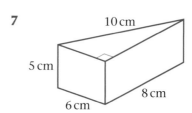

25 m
0.8 m
1.8 m
8 m

In questions **6–11** work out **(a)** the volume **(b)** the total surface area
of the prism.

6

6 cm
6 cm
6 cm

7

10 cm
5 cm
6 cm
8 cm

8

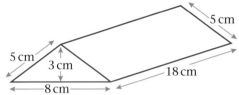

9

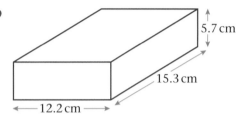

10

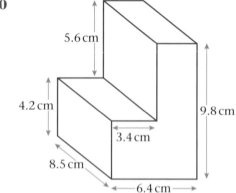

11

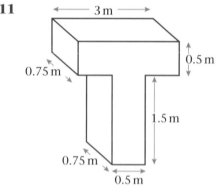

10.6 Surface area and volume of cylinders

- For a cylinder of height h with a base of radius r:
  - surface area $= 2\pi rh + 2\pi r^2$
  - volume $= \pi r^2 h$

Example 7

Find the total surface area of a cylinder which has diameter 12 mm and height 3 cm.

> Work in cm. 6 mm = 0.6 cm

Radius $= 0.6$ cm

Volume $= \pi \times (0.6)^2 \times 3 = 1.08\pi \text{ cm}^3$ (answer in terms of π)
$\qquad\qquad = 3.4 \text{ cm}^3$ (1 d.p.)

Surface area $= 2\pi r^2 + 2\pi rh$
$\qquad\qquad = 2\pi \times (0.6)^2 + 2\pi \times 0.6 \times 3$
$\qquad\qquad = 0.72\pi + 3.6\pi = 4.32\pi \text{ cm}^2$ (in terms of π)
$\qquad\qquad\qquad = 13.6 \text{ cm}^2$ (1 d.p.)

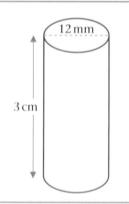

Exercise 10F

1 Work out the volume of these cylinders.
Give your answers in terms of π.
  (a) radius 10 cm, height 7 cm
  (b) radius 4 cm, height 12 cm
  (c) radius 9 cm, height 15 cm
  (d) diameter 50 mm, height 1 m
  (e) diameter 0.8 m, height 3.6 mm

2 Work out the radii of these cylinders.
  (a) height 30 cm, volume 200 cm³
  (b) height 12 cm, volume 180 cm³
  (c) height 6 cm, volume 140 cm³
  (d) height 25 mm, volume 12 cm³
  (e) height 1 m, volume 1500 cm³

> Work in centimetres throughout.

3 Work out the surface area and volume of these cylinders.
Give your answers to 3 significant figures.
  (a) radius 7 cm, height 18 cm
  (b) radius 10 cm, height 22 cm
  (c) radius 5 cm, height 3 m
  (d) radius 25 mm, height 7 cm
  (e) diameter 40 mm, height 200 cm
  (f) diameter 4 m, height 9 mm

4 Work out the volume of the tunnel.

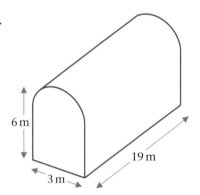

5 The diagram shows a skateboard ramp.
The curved surface has two edges which are quarter circles.
Work out the area of the curved surface.

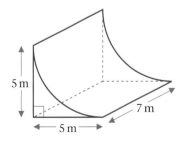

6 Work out the volume and surface area of this wedge.
The curved edges are quarter circles.

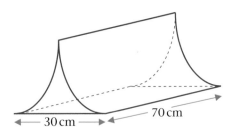

Mixed exercise 10

1 Work out the area of the triangles shown.

(a)
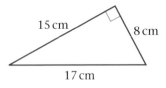

(b)
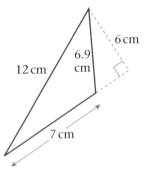

(c)
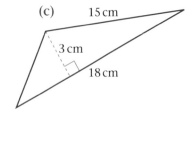

2 Work out the area of the trapeziums shown.

(a)
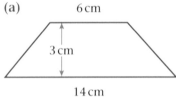

(b)
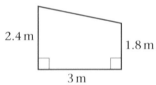

(c)
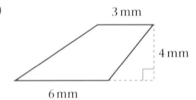

3 In each diagram, work out the value of *x*.

(a)
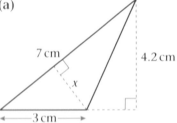

(b)
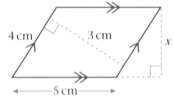

(c)
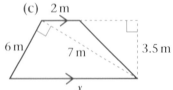

4 Work out the volume of a silver ingot which is in the shape of a cuboid measuring 10 cm × 4 cm × 5 mm.

5 Work out the capacity of a water container that measures 1.5 metres by 40 cm by 50 cm.
Give your answer in litres.

6 The surface area of a cube is 294 cm².
Work out the volume of the cube.

7 Work out the surface area of a cuboid measuring 2 metres by 50 cm by 15 mm.

Work in centimetres.

8 A cornflake packet measures 7 cm by 23 cm by 29 cm.
How many packets will fit into a carton which measures 58 cm by 46 cm by 63 cm?

9 A packet of pencils measures 14 cm by 5 cm by 1 cm.
What would be a sensible size for a box to contain 144 packets?

10 A box of chocolates measures 3 cm by 18 cm by 12 cm.
How many can be packed into a carton which measures 30 cm by 36 cm by 54 cm?

11 Work out the volume and surface area of these prisms.

(a)

3 cm

3 cm

3 cm

3 cm

3 cm

3 cm

20 cm

(b)

5 cm

17 cm

12 cm

4 cm

15 cm

20 cm

12 A machine makes circular washers which are 1.2 mm thick.
Each washer is a circular disc with a circular hole in the centre.
The external diameter is 5.8 cm and the internal diameter is 2.2 cm.
Work out, in cm³, the volume of 1200 washers.

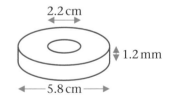

2.2 cm

1.2 mm

5.8 cm

Summary of key points

1 The area of a triangle is $\frac{1}{2}$ base $\times$ perpendicular height or $\frac{1}{2}bh$.

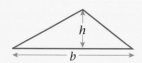

2 The area of a parallelogram is base $\times$ perpendicular height or bh.

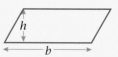

3 The area of a trapezium is $\frac{1}{2}h(a + b)$ where a and b are the lengths of the parallel sides and h is the distance between the parallel sides.

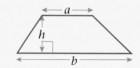

4 Cuboid: surface area $= 2(ab + bc + ac)$
      volume $= abc$

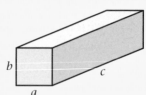

5 The **surface area** is the total area of all the faces of a solid shape.

6 A **prism** is a 3-D shape with the same cross-section all along its length.

7 Volume of a prism $=$ area of cross-section $\times$ length.

Examination practice paper
Stage 1 (multiple choice)

1 Given that $23 \times 337 = 7751$.
Find the value of $7751 \div 2.3$.

   A 0.337 **B** 3.37   **C** 33.7   **D** 0.0377 **E** 3370

2 A teacher has bought 28 workbooks for a class.
The total cost was £49.
How much did each workbook cost?

   A £21   **B** 17p   **C** 18p
   D £7   **E** £1.75

3 Simplify $4a + 3c - 2a - 7c$.

   A $2a - 4c$ **B** $6a + 10c$ **C** $2a + 4c$
   D $6a - 4c$ **E** $2a + 3c$

4 Factorise $p^2 + 5p$.

   A $6p$ **B** $p(p + 5)$ **C** $p(1 + 5)$
   D $p(p + 5p)$ **E** $p^2(p + 5)$

5

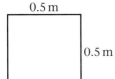

0.5 m

0.5 m

Diagram NOT
accurately drawn

The diagram shows the dimensions of a board.
The board is to be covered with plastic tiles.
Each tile is square, with a side of length 2 cm.
Work out the number of tiles needed to completely cover
the board.

   A 6.25   **B** 50   **C** 625   **D** 100   **E** 125

6 Usma travels 160 kilometres in her car.
It takes $2\frac{1}{2}$ hours for her to travel this distance.
Work out her average speed.

   A 160 km/h   **B** 60 km/h   **C** 64 km/h
   D 80 km/h   **E** 400 km/h

7 Find the Highest Common Factor (HCF) of 18 and 63.

   A 6   **B** 9   **C** 18   **D** 21   **E** 1134

8 Find the Lowest Common Multiple (LCM) of 12 and 16.

   A 4   **B** 8   **C** 12   **D** 16   **E** 48

9 Here is an arithmetic sequence.

      2, 6, 10, 14

Work out an expression, in terms of n, for the nth term of the sequence?

   A $n + 4$ **B** $4n$

   C $n - 2$ **D** $4n - 2$

   E $4n + 2$

10 Expand and simplify $(x + 4)(x + 5)$.

   A $x^2 + 9x + 20$ **B** $x^2 + 9x + 9$

   C $x^2 + 20x + 9$ **D** $x^2 + 20x + 20$

   E $x^2 + 4x + 9x + 20$

11 What is the number 700 written as a product of its prime factors?

   A $4 \times 25 \times 7$ **B** 7×100

   C $2 \times 2 \times 25 \times 7$ **D** $7 \times 5 \times 5 \times 4$

   E $2 \times 2 \times 5 \times 5 \times 7$

12

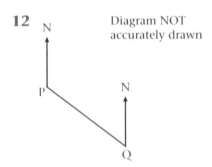

Diagram NOT accurately drawn

The bearing of Q from P is 130°.
Calculate the bearing of P from Q.

   A 050°   **B** 130°   **C** 290°   **D** 310°   **E** 300°

13

Diagram NOT accurately drawn

Work out the coordinates of the midpoint of the line AB.

A $(6, 5\frac{1}{2})$ B $(6, 5)$ C $(6, 6)$

D $(7, 5\frac{1}{2})$ E $(5, 5)$

14

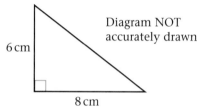

Diagram NOT accurately drawn

Work out the area of the triangle.

A $48\,cm^2$ B $12\,cm^2$ C $24\,cm^2$

D $36\,cm^2$ E $20\,cm^2$

15 Find the Highest Common Factor (HCF) of 36 and 96.

A   6   B   12   C   3   D   60   E   96

16

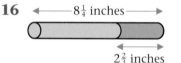

Diagram NOT accurately drawn

A rod has a length of $8\frac{1}{4}$ inches. $2\frac{2}{3}$ inch is cut off.
What length of the rod is left? Give your answer in its simplest form.

A $6\frac{5}{12}$ B $6\frac{1}{4}$ C $-6\frac{5}{12}$ D $5\frac{5}{12}$ E $5\frac{7}{12}$

17 Expand and simplify $(x + 3)(x - 7)$.

A $x^2 - 4x - 21$ B $x^2 + 4x - 21$

C $x^2 + 4x + 21$ D $x^2 - 4x - 4$

E $x^2 - 4x + 4$

18 Factorise $x^2 + x - 20$.

A $(x - 4)(x + 5)$ B $(x + 4)(x - 5)$

C $(x - 4)(x - 5)$ D $(x - 2)(x + 10)$

E $(x - 10)(x + 2)$

19 The weight of an apple is given as 80 grams, to the nearest gram.
What is the minimum the weight could be?

A   75 g   B   79 g   C   79.5 g

D   80.5 g   E   80.05 g

20 Factorise completely $8t^2 - 12tw$.

A $2t(4t - 3w)$ B $4t(2t - 3w)$

C $4t(t - 4w)$ D $4t(t - 3tw)$

E $t(t - 3w)$

21 There are two points on a 3-D coordinate grid.
Points A is (6, 4, 2) and point B is (4, 1, −4).
Calculate the distance between point A and point B.

A   7   B   8   C   6   D   5   E   4

22 Expand and simplify $(3x - 1)(2x + 5)$.

A $6x^2 + 15x - 5$ B $6x^2 + 13x - 5$

C $6x^2 - 13x - 5$ D $6x^2 - 15x - 5$

E $6x^2 + 13x - 6$

23 A swimming pool is to be emptied at the rate of 0.4 litres per second.
The swimming pool contains 20 000 litres of water.
To the nearest minute, how long does it take to empty the swimming pool?

A   2 h 13 min   B   133 h   C   13 h 53 min

D   83 h 3 min   E   500 h

24 Factorise completely $12x^2 + 5x - 2$.

A $(12x - 1)(x + 2)$ B $(6x - 2)(2x + 1)$

C $(12x - 2)(1x + 1)$ D $(4x - 1)(3x + 2)$

E $(4x - 2)(3x + 1)$

25 Simplify $(2p^2q^3)^3$.

A $2p^5q^6$ B $2p^6q^6$ C $8p^5q^6$

D $2p^6q^9$ E $8p^6q^9$

Examination practice paper Stage 2

1 Jenni travelled 150 miles in $2\frac{1}{2}$ hours.
  At what average speed did she travel?

  (2 marks)

2 Here is a diagram of a cube of side 3 cm. Work out the surface area of the cube.

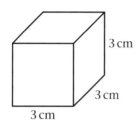

3 cm
3 cm
3 cm

  (2 marks)

3 Work out $\sqrt{4.5^2 - 12.96}$

  (1 mark)

4 On a copy of the coordinate grid draw the line with equation $y = 2x + 1$

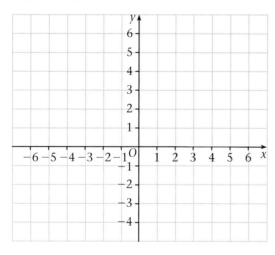

  (3 marks)

5 (a) Work out $4^6 \div 4^2$.
   (b) If $3x^2 = 75$ what is the value of x?
   (c) What is the value of 25^0?

  (3 marks)

6 (a) Simplify $e^5 \times e^4$
   (b) Simplify $5(x + 5) + 3(2x - 4)$.

  (3 marks)

7 Evaluate $2.3 \times 10^6 \div 4.6 \times 10^{-2}$
Give your answer in standard form.

(2 marks)

8 *PA* and *PB* are tangents
to a circle
from the point *P*.
Angle $P = 40°$
Work out the size
of the angle
marked *x*.

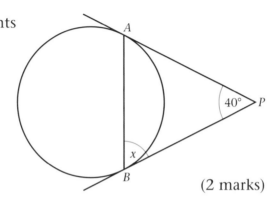

(2 marks)

9 Factorise $x^2 - 36$.

(2 marks)

10 Write the recurring decimal $0.1\dot{2}\dot{7}$ as a fraction
in the form $\frac{a}{b}$.

(2 marks)

11 Simplify $\dfrac{x^2 - 5x + 6}{x^2 - 4}$.

(2 marks)

12 *AB* is a tangent at *Q* to
a circle centre *C*.
PQ is a diameter of the circle.
Angle $CQR = 25°$
Angle $BQR = 70°$
Explain why *C* cannot be
the centre of the circle.

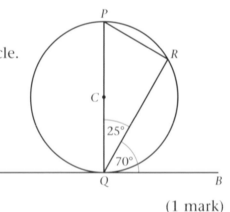

(1 mark)

Practice questions
Stage 1 (multiple choice)

1 Pens are packed into boxes, each containing 32 pens.
How many boxes can be packed from 8192 pens?

    A   270   **B**   272   **C** 256   **D**   263   **E**   265

2 A book costs £13.50 to buy. How much would it cost to buy 25 of these books?

    A   £337.50   **B**   £702.00   **C**   £94.50

    D   £72.00   **E**   £69.12

3 Given that $23 \times 347 = 7981$
find the value of 2.3×34.7

    A   798.1   **B**   79.81   **C**   7.981

    D   0.7981   **E**   0.07981

4 Here is an arithmetic sequence.

      8, 13, 18, 23, 28

Work out an expression, in terms of n, for the nth term of the sequence.

    A $5n - 3$ **B** $5n$ **C** $5n + 3$

    D $n + 3$ **E** $3n$

5

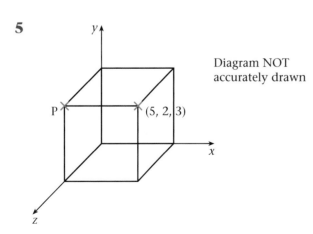

Diagram NOT accurately drawn

Work out the coordinates of the point P.

    A   (5, 0, 3)   **B**   (5, 2, 0)   **C**   (5, 2, 3)

    D   (0, 2, 3)   **E**   (5, 0, 0)

6 Simplify $7a + 5b - 3a - 4b$.

    A $10a + 9b$ **B** $4a - b$ **C** $4a + b$

    D $10a - b$ **E** $10a + b$

7 Factorise $9t + 3$.

    A $12t$ **B** $3t + 1$ **C** $t(9 + 3)$

    D $3t(3t + 1)$ **E** $3(3t + 1)$

8 Factorise $h^2 - 5h$.

    A $5h^3$ **B** $5(h^2 - h)$ **C** $5h(h - 1)$

    D $h(h - 5)$ **E** $4h$

9 Sareena wants to find an estimate for the calculation

$$\frac{13.8 \times 12.2}{5.9 \times 7.1}$$

    A   1   **B**   2   **C**   3   **D**   4   **E**   5

10 Find the Lowest Common Multiple (LCM) of 36 and 60.

    A   3   **B**   6   **C**   24   **D**   60   **E**   180

11 Find the Highest Common Factor (HCF) of 20 and 30.

    A   2   **B**   5   **C**   10   **D**   20   **E**   600

12 What is the number 300 written as a product of its prime factors?

    A $4 \times 3 \times 25$ **B** $2 \times 2 \times 3 \times 5 \times 5$

    C $4 \times 3 \times 5 \times 5$ **D** $2 \times 2 \times 3 \times 25$

    E 12×25

13 Work out the value of $2\frac{2}{3} + 1\frac{3}{4}$.

    Give your answer in its simplest form.

    A $3\frac{5}{7}$ **B** $4\frac{5}{12}$ **C** $3\frac{5}{12}$ **D** $\frac{15}{7}$ **E** $\frac{15}{12}$

14 Work out the value of $1\frac{1}{4} + \frac{3}{8}$.

    Give your answer in its simplest form.

    A $3\frac{1}{3}$ **B** $1\frac{3}{32}$ **C** $\frac{3}{32}$ **D** $\frac{10}{3}$ **E** $1\frac{3}{12}$

15 Write the number 14 600 in standard form notation.

    A 146×10^4 **B** 146×10^{-4} **C** 1.46×10^4

    D 1.46×10^{-3} **E** 1.46×10^{-2}

16 Write the number 0.00879 in standard form notation.

    A 879×10^3 **B** 8.79×10^3 **C** 879×10^{-3}

    D 8.79×10^{-3} **E** 8.79×10^{-2}

17 Hazel travels for 2 h 20 min on a train.
Her average speed is 90 miles per hour.
How far did she travel?

    A   210 miles   **B**   198 miles   **C**   195 miles

    D   185 miles   **E**   225 miles

18 The amount of water in a jug is given as 1.3 litres, to the nearest $\frac{1}{10}$ litre.
What is the maximum the amount of water could be?

    A   1.345 litres   **B**   1.349 litres   **C**   1.39 litres

    D   1.29 litres   **E**   1.35 litres

19

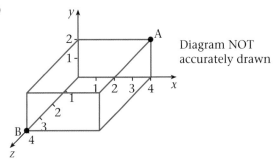

Diagram NOT accurately drawn

The diagram shows a cuboid on a 3-D grid.
Calculate the distance between point A and point B.

    A   6   **B**   7   **C**   8   **D**   5   **E**   4

20 Grain is emptied from a hopper at the rate of 0.3 cubic metres per second.
How many cubic metres will be emptied from the hopper in 3 hours 20 minutes?

    A   12 000   **B**   36 000   **C**   5760

    D   3600   **E**   96

21 Expand and simplify $(x + 5)(x - 2)$.

    A $x^2 - 3x - 10$ **B** $x^2 + 3x - 10$

    C $x^2 + 3x - 7$ **D** $x^2 - 10x - 10$

    E $x^2 + 3x + 7$

22 Expand and simplify $(2x - 3)(x + 4)$.

    A $2x^2 + 8x - 3x - 12$ B $2x^2 + 11x - 12$

    C $2x^2 + 5x - 12$ D $2x^2 + 11x + 12$

    E $2x^2 + 5x + 12$

23 Factorise $x^2 + 4x - 12$.

    A $(x + 2)(x - 6)$ B $(x - 3)(x + 4)$

    C $(x - 4)(x + 3)$ D $(x - 2)(x + 6)$

    E $(x + 3)(x + 4)$

24 Factorise $6x^2 - 17x + 12$.

    A $(2x - 3)(3x + 4)$ B $(6x - 3)(x - 4)$

    C $(2x - 6)(3x + 2)$ D $(2x - 1)(3x - 12)$

    E $(2x - 3)(3x - 4)$

25 Factorise completely $12x^3 + 16x^2y^2$.

    A $2x^2(6x + 8y^2)$ B $4x(3x^2 + 4xy^2)$

    C $x^2(12x + 16y^2)$ D $4x^2(3x + 4y^2)$

    E $4x^3(3 + 4y^2)$

26 Simplify $(5p^2q^4)^3$.

    A $5p^5q^7$ B $5p^5q^7$ C $125p^6q^{12}$

    D $25p^5q^7$ E $25p^6q^{12}$

Formulae sheet

Volume of a prism = area of cross-section × length

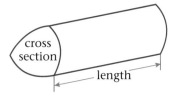

Volume of sphere = $\frac{4}{3}\pi r^3$

Surface of a sphere = $4\pi r^2$

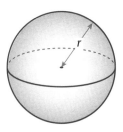

Volume of cone = $\frac{1}{3}\pi r^2 h$

Curved surface area of cone = $\pi r l$

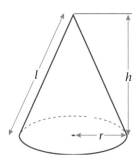

In any triangle ABC

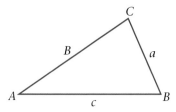

Sine rule = $\dfrac{a}{\sin A} = \dfrac{b}{\sin B} = \dfrac{c}{\sin C}$

Cosine rule $a^2 = b^2 + c^2 - 2bc \cos A$

Area of triangle = $\frac{1}{2}ab \sin C$

The quadratic equation
The solutions of $ax^2 + bx + c = 0$ where $a \neq 0$, are given by

$$x = \frac{-b \pm \sqrt{(b^2 - 4ac)}}{2a}$$

Answers

Exercise 1A

1 (a) 63, 0, −63
   (b) 562, −5620
   (c) 1 million, 30 000, −2
2 (a) Four hundred and thirty-two
   (b) Eight thousand, two hundred
   (c) Six thousand, three hundred and seventy
   (d) Sixteen thousand, eight hundred and ninety-two
   (e) Three hundred and seventy-two thousand, eight hundred and fifty-nine
   (f) Four hundred and eighty-three thousand and two
   (g) Three million, two hundred and fifteen thousand, four hundred and sixty-eight
   (h) Three million, six hundred and eighty-two
3 (a) 463   (b) 15 027   (c) 116 225
   (d) 305 101   (e) 2 327 035   (f) 500 000

Exercise 1B

1 (a) −7   (b) 4   (c) 10   (d) 9
   (e) −1   (f) 2   (g) −2   (h) −10
2 (a) 24   (b) −15   (c) −8   (d) 3
   (e) −40   (f) −6   (g) −30   (h) 10
3 11 metres
4 −12 °C

5 (a)

		1st number	
×	−2	6	−7
5	−10	30	−35
−3	6	−18	21
8	−16	48	−56

2nd number (rows 5, −3, 8)

(b)

		1st number	
−	2	−3	8
−4	6	1	12
5	−3	−8	3
−1	3	−2	9

2nd number (rows −4, 5, −1)

(c)

		1st number	
+	−3	−4	2
5	2	1	7
1	−2	−3	3
−6	−9	−10	−4

2nd number (rows 5, 1, −6)

(d)

		1st number	
÷	16	−24	−36
−2	−8	12	18
4	4	−6	−9
−8	−2	3	4.5

2nd number (rows −2, 4, −8)

Exercise 1C

1 (a) 40   (b) 200   (c) 6000   (d) 3
   (e) 20   (f) 9000   (g) 2000   (h) 4000
2 (a) (i) 40 × 40   (ii) 1600
   (b) (i) 80 ÷ 20   (ii) 4

(c) (i) 200 ÷ 40   (ii) 5
(d) (i) 500 × 30   (ii) 15 000
(e) (i) $\dfrac{900 \times 20}{10} = 90 \times 20$ (ii) 18 000

(f) (i) $\dfrac{30 \times 20}{10 \times 30}$ (ii) 2
3 £800 000
4 2 × 20 = 40 pints

Exercise 1D

1 (a) 46   (b) 440   (c) 3.7
   (d) 5500   (e) 0.0024   (f) 0.095
2 (a) 945   (b) 10 700   (c) 789 000
   (d) 0.835   (e) 0.002 38   (f) 0.0480
3 (a) 4900   (b) 80 000   (c) 380
   (d) 0.0289   (e) 2.60   (f) 5000
4 (a) 2800   (b) 5   (c) 18
   (d) 4   (e) 40   (f) 200 400
   (g) 0.18   (h) 75

Exercise 1E

1 (a) 9   (b) 64   (c) 49   (d) 64
   (e) 100   (f) 4   (g) 36   (h) 27
   (i) 1000   (j) 16   (k) 125   (l) 144
   (m) 169   (n) 8   (o) 25   (p) 81
   (q) 121   (r) 196   (s) 225
2 (a) ±8   (b) ±3   (c) ±5   (d) ±12
   (e) ±13   (f) ±15   (g) ±2   (h) ±10
   (i) ±6   (j) ±11   (k) ±7   (l) ±9
   (m) ±4   (n) ±14   (o) 2   (p) 5
   (q) 3   (r) 4   (s) 10
3 (a) ±7   (b) ±6   (c) ±11   (d) ±8   (e) ±5
4 (a) ±8.77 (b) 4.58   (c) −2.02   (d) −2.20 (e) 3880
   (f) ±22.9 (g) 5140   (h) −2.44   (i) ±164

Exercise 1F

1 (a) 5^4 (b) 2^5 (c) 6^3 (d) $7^3 \times 2^2$
   (e) $3^2 \times 8^4$ (f) $4^4 \times 2^3$ (g) $2^3 \times 3^2 \times 4^3$
2 (a) 16   (b) 243   (c) 216   (d) 2401
   (e) 512   (f) 11 664   (g) 65 536   (h) 10 125
   (i) 31 104   (j) 108
3 (a) $x = 3$ (b) $x = 4$ (c) $x = 6$ (d) $x = 4$
   (e) $x = 2$ (f) $x = 3$ (g) $x = 4$ (h) $x = 0$

Exercise 1G

1 8^6 2 3^6 3 2^9 4 5^3
5 3^2 6 7^2 7 8^2 8 10^3
9 8^9 10 2^9 11 4^6 12 6^2
13 2^{-1} 14 4^{10} 15 9   16 1
17 x^7 18 y^2 19 a^3 20 z

Exercise 1H

1 (a) 33   (b) 4   (c) 24   (d) 16
   (e) 2.7   (f) 81   (g) ±3   (h) 16
   (i) ±1   (j) ±6   (k) 77   (l) 11
2 (a) 3 × (4 + 5) = 27
   (b) (2 + 3) × (2 + 3) = 25
   (c) (6 − 7) ÷ (8 − 9) = 1 or (6 − 7) × (8 − 9) = 1
   (d) 10 + 9 + 8 + 7 = 34
   (e) (3 − 3) × 3 = 0
   (f) (3 + 3) ÷ 3 = 2

Exercise 1I

1 (a) $\frac{1}{4}$ (b) $\frac{1}{3}$ (c) $\frac{1}{2}$
  (d) $\frac{1}{7}$ (e) $\frac{1}{9}$ (f) $\frac{1}{20}$
2 (a) 10   (b) 2   (c) 4
  (d) $\frac{5}{2}$ or $2\frac{1}{2}$ (e) $\frac{10}{3}$ or $3\frac{1}{3}$ (f) 8
3 (a) $1\frac{2}{3}$ (b) $3\frac{1}{2}$ (c) 4
  (d) 8   (e) $5\frac{1}{3}$ (f) $1\frac{3}{5}$

Exercise 1J

1 (a) 1, 2, 3, 4, 6, 8, 12, 16, 24, 48
  (b) 1, 2, 3, 4, 5, 6, 8, 9, 10, 12, 15, 18, 20, 24, 30, 36,
      40, 45, 60, 72, 90, 120, 180, 360
  (c) 1, 29
  (d) 1, 2, 4, 5, 10, 20, 25, 50, 100
  (e) 1, 71
  (f) 1, 3, 5, 15, 43, 129, 215, 645
2 29, 71
3 (a) 4, 8, 12, 16, 20   (b) 7, 14, 21, 28, 35
  (c) 11, 22, 33, 44, 55   (d) 20, 40, 60, 80, 100
4 (a) 2×5^2 (b) $2^3 \times 3^2$
  (c) $2 \times 3^2 \times 5^2$ (d) $2^3 \times 3 \times 5 \times 7$
5 (a) 3   (b) 2   (c) 4   (d) 3   (e) 4
6 (a) 24   (b) 35   (c) 12   (d) 12   (e) 30
7 (a) $2^3 \times 3^3 \times 5^2 \times 7$ (b) $2 \times 3 = 6$

Mixed exercise 1

1 (a) 256 214; 0; three hundred and two thousand four
      hundred and twelve; $-73\,864$
  (b) Two hundred and fifty-six thousand two hundred
      and fourteen
  (c) 302 412
2 (a) -9 (b) 10   (c) 4   (d) 2
3 (a) -16 (b) 2   (c) -2 (d) 35
4 (a) (i) $\dfrac{300 \times 20}{500}$ (ii) 12

  (b) (i) $\dfrac{2 \times 8}{2^2}$ (ii)   4

  (c) (i) $\dfrac{8000 \div 400}{\sqrt[3]{8}}$ (ii) 10

5 £600
6 (a) 37   (b) 500   (c) 0.0075
  (d) 96 300   (e) 489.30
7 (a) 16   (b) 144   (c) 64   (d) 169
  (e) ± 7 (f) ± 14 (g) ± 15 (h) 64
  (i) 125   (j) 2
8 (a) 5^3 (b) 4^4 (c) $2^2 \times 3^3$ (d) $5^2 \times 7^2$
9 (a) 512   (b) 10 000   (c) 625
  (d) 144   (e) 800
10 (a) $x = 2$ (b) $x = 4$ (c) $x = 3$
11 (a) 1, 9, 81   (b) 1, 27   (c) 13, 17, 23, 31
   (d) 1, 9, 27   (e) 9, 27, 81
12 (a) 2^7 (b) 5^5 (c) 7^7 (d) 3^5 (e) 9^4
   (f) 8^2 (g) 7^3 (h) 6   (i) 5^5
13 (a) 6.25   (b) 102.01   (c) 262.144   (d) 4.02
   (e) ± 6.16 (f) 9.261   (g) 39.69   (h) 13.824
   (i) 2.4   (j) -2
14 (a) 32   (b) 5   (c) 7   (d) 2
15 (a) $2^2 \times 3^2 \times 5$ (b) $2^2 \times 7^2$
   (c) $2^3 \times 3 \times 5^2$
16 (a) 6   (b) 6   (c) 3
17 (a) 20   (b) 24   (c) 24
18 (a) $\frac{1}{9}$ (b) $\frac{1}{6}$ (c) 2   (d) 1.6
   (e) $\frac{5}{4}$ (f) $\frac{7}{6}$ (g) $\frac{1}{x}$ (h) y

Exercise 2A

1 (a) $\frac{3}{2}$ (b) $\frac{5}{4}$ (c) $\frac{7}{5}$ (d) $\frac{7}{3}$ (e) $\frac{15}{4}$
  (f) $\frac{23}{5}$ (g) $\frac{59}{9}$ (h) $\frac{83}{10}$ (i) $\frac{87}{8}$ (j) $\frac{285}{28}$
2 (a) $3\frac{1}{2}$ (b) $2\frac{1}{4}$ (c) $2\frac{1}{8}$ (d) $3\frac{1}{5}$ (e) $6\frac{1}{2}$
  (f) $2\frac{3}{10}$ (g) $4\frac{3}{5}$ (h) $5\frac{1}{3}$ (i) $2\frac{1}{10}$ (j) $7\frac{1}{2}$

Exercise 2B

1 (a) $\frac{1}{3} = \frac{2}{6} = \frac{4}{12} = \frac{6}{18}$ (b) $\frac{2}{5} = \frac{4}{10} = \frac{20}{50} = \frac{40}{100}$
  (c) $\frac{3}{8} = \frac{6}{16} = \frac{12}{32} = \frac{24}{64}$ (d) $\frac{3}{10} = \frac{15}{50} = \frac{30}{100} = \frac{300}{1000}$
2 (a) $\frac{1}{2}$ (b) $\frac{3}{5}$ (c) $\frac{2}{3}$ (d) $\frac{3}{5}$ (e) $\frac{5}{6}$
  (f) $\frac{4}{5}$ (g) $\frac{3}{5}$ (h) $\frac{4}{5}$ (i) $\frac{2}{3}$ (j) $\frac{5}{6}$

Exercise 2C

1 (a) $\frac{1}{4}$ (b) $\frac{2}{3}$ (c) $\frac{11}{15}$ (d) $\frac{6}{7}$
2 $\frac{1}{4}$, $\frac{3}{10}$, $\frac{2}{5}$, $\frac{1}{2}$
3 Mia
4 (a) Dress circle   (b) Boxes
5 $\frac{7}{8}$, $\frac{13}{16}$, $\frac{2}{3}$, $\frac{1}{4}$

Exercise 2D

1 (a) $1\frac{1}{4}$ (b) $\frac{11}{15}$ (c) $\frac{7}{36}$ (d) $\frac{9}{14}$
  (e) $1\frac{3}{10}$ (f) $\frac{13}{28}$ (g) $\frac{19}{28}$ (h) $\frac{1}{8}$
2 (a) $1\frac{3}{4}$ (b) $3\frac{1}{2}$ (c) $4\frac{1}{12}$ (d) $3\frac{1}{2}$
  (e) $5\frac{13}{15}$ (f) $6\frac{7}{12}$ (g) $4\frac{11}{14}$ (h) $5\frac{13}{21}$
3 (a) $1\frac{5}{8}$ (b) $2\frac{1}{12}$ (c) $1\frac{7}{24}$ (d) $3\frac{7}{10}$
  (e) $2\frac{3}{4}$ (f) $4\frac{7}{10}$ (g) $1\frac{11}{14}$ (h) $3\frac{11}{24}$
4 $10\frac{1}{4}$ lb
5 $3\frac{7}{8}$ kg
6 $1\frac{1}{8}$ metres
7 $2\frac{5}{12}$ kg

Exercise 2E

1 (a) $\frac{2}{15}$ (b) $\frac{1}{2}$ (c) $\frac{3}{10}$ (d) $\frac{1}{2}$ (e) $\frac{5}{6}$
  (f) $1\frac{5}{6}$ (g) $\frac{4}{11}$ (h) $\frac{1}{9}$ (i) $1\frac{1}{5}$ (j) $1\frac{1}{4}$
2 (a) $1\frac{1}{8}$ (b) $2\frac{3}{4}$ (c) $5\frac{5}{18}$ (d) $16\frac{1}{5}$
  (e) $3\frac{1}{4}$ (f) $10\frac{4}{5}$ (g) $3\frac{3}{4}$ (h) $\frac{3}{4}$
3 (a) $1\frac{1}{11}$ (b) $1\frac{11}{13}$ (c) $1\frac{9}{11}$ (d) $1\frac{13}{17}$
  (e) $3\frac{1}{7}$ (f) $8\frac{1}{6}$ (g) 12   (h) $13\frac{1}{3}$
4 8
5 $7\frac{1}{8}$ kg
6 $1\frac{1}{2}$ hours
7 $3\frac{1}{14}$

Exercise 2F

1 (a) 53.1   (b) 0.216
  (c) 0.5358   (d) 267.1
  (e) 3.6   (f) 0.0053
  (g) 638   (h) 280
  (i) 0.003   (j) 0.007 86
2 (a) 3.6 kg   (b) 0.0036 kg or 3.6 g
3 11.3 g
4 3568 g

Exercise 2G

1. (a) 6.2, 0.62, 0.6, 0.59
   (b) 7.9, 0.79, 0.76, 0.079
   (c) 3.27, 3.21, 3.12, 0.37
   (d) 1.01, 0.99, 0.91, 0.09
   (e) 0.024, 0.021, 0.02, 0.002
2. Rachael   1.52
   Sunil   1.60
   Tom   1.67
   Kwame   1.68
3. 3.6 s, 3.62 s, 3.902 s, 3.96 s

Exercise 2H

1. (a) 7.9   (b) 5.2   (c) 5.27   (d) 0.81
   (e) 2.78   (f) 7.64   (g) 33.59   (h) 23.33
   (i) 5.811   (j) 21.32
2. (a) 4.2   (b) 3.2   (c) 17.5   (d) 7.43
   (e) 3.86   (f) 2.54   (g) 13.59   (h) 13.81
   (i) 5.38   (j) 0.324
3. 2.275 kg
4. 6.35 kg
5. 40.3 seconds
6. No, they need a length of 4.13 m.
7. Yes, the total weight is 19.9 kg.

Exercise 2I

1. (a) 1.5   (b) 0.42   (c) 0.468   (d) 0.3303
   (e) 7.62   (f) 4.716   (g) 59.94   (h) 0.227 84
2. (a) 2.6   (b) 52.3   (c) 7.125   (d) 17.6
   (e) 2.95   (f) 23.44   (g) 7.3125   (h) 20.375
3. 4.68 m
4. 1.8 kg
5. 5 glasses
6. 146.2 km
7. 18 pens
8. (a) 0.1856   (b) 18 560   (c) 0.58
   (d) 5800   (e) 0.000 185 6

Exercise 2J

1. (a) 0.6   (b) 0.1$\dot{6}$ (c) 0.625   (d) 0.45
   (e) 0.75   (f) 0.$\dot{3}$ (g) 0.$\dot{4}$ (h) 0.58$\dot{3}$
   (i) 0.3$\dot{1}\dot{8}$ (j) 0.2$\dot{5}\dot{9}$
2. (a) $\frac{7}{10}$ (b) $\frac{1}{2}$ (c) $\frac{3}{25}$ (d) $\frac{13}{20}$
   (e) $\frac{7}{8}$ (f) $\frac{181}{500}$ (g) $\frac{137}{1000}$ (h) $\frac{137}{200}$
3. (a) exact   (b) recurring   (c) exact
   (d) recurring   (e) recurring
4. (a) $\frac{1}{9}$ (b) $\frac{7}{11}$ (c) $\frac{14}{45}$ (d) $\frac{8}{37}$
   (e) $\frac{5}{11}$ (f) $\frac{146}{1111}$ (g) $\frac{49}{333}$ (h) $\frac{20}{27}$
   (i) $\frac{6359}{9900}$ (j) $\frac{101}{180}$

Exercise 2K

1. (a) $\frac{13}{25}$, 0.7, $\frac{8}{10}$, 0.81, 0.84   (b) $\frac{1}{2}$, 0.7, 0.73, $\frac{3}{4}$ = 0.75
   (c) 2, 2.3, $2\frac{4}{10}$, 2.42, $2\frac{43}{100}$ (d) $\frac{3}{10}$, 0.33, $\frac{1}{3}$, 0.34, $\frac{7}{20}$
   (e) 4, 4.04, $4\frac{4}{10}$, 4.44, $4\frac{4}{9}$
2. (a) 1.3 kg, 1.32 kg, 1.39 kg, 1.41 kg
   (b) 9.9 s, 9.92 s, 10.01 s, 10.1 s, 10.11 s
   (c) $\frac{1}{4}$ kg, 0.3 kg, 0.35 kg, $\frac{1}{2}$ kg
   (d) $\frac{1}{6}$ inch, $\frac{1}{4}$ inch, $\frac{3}{8}$ inch, $\frac{2}{5}$ inch

Exercise 2L

1. 16 egg boxes
2. 4 cars
3. 5 packs
4. £7.43
5. 45 mph. Speedometer is only really accurate to within 5 mph
6. 9.5 cm. Luisa will only be able to draw to the nearest millimetre
7. £6.66
8. £591.06
9. He will not be able to cut this accurately.
10. She will not be able to measure this accurately. The accuracy will depend on her weighing scales i.e. if they go up in intervals of 10 g she should aim for 130 g.

Exercise 2M

1. 4.41
2. 79.507
3. −97.656 25
4. ±2.5
5. 3.8
6. ±1.3
7. ±2.7
8. 20.678 (3 d.p.)
9. ±3.75
10. 81.92
11. 15.376
12. 3.24
13. ±6.456 (3 d.p.)
14. 9.049 (3 d.p.) or 6.551 (3 d.p.)
15. 12.634 (3 d.p.) or 4.202 (3 d.p.)
16. (a) 1.25 hours   (b) 3.5 hours   (c) 5.2 hours
    (d) 4.2$\dot{6}$ hours   (e) 11.95 hours
17. (a) 2 hours 15 minutes   (b) 3 hours 30 minutes
    (c) 5 hours 45 minutes   (d) 4 hours 42 minutes

Exercise 2N

1. (a) (i) 0.65   (ii) $\frac{13}{20}$
   (b) (i) 0.2   (ii) $\frac{1}{5}$
   (c) (i) 0.25   (ii) $\frac{1}{4}$
   (d) (i) 0.32   (ii) $\frac{8}{25}$
   (e) (i) 0.74   (ii) $\frac{37}{50}$
   (f) (i) 0.225   (ii) $\frac{9}{40}$
   (g) (i) 0.675   (ii) $\frac{27}{40}$
   (h) (i) 0.$\dot{3}$ (ii) $\frac{1}{3}$
   (i) (i) 0.$\dot{6}$ (ii) $\frac{2}{3}$
   (j) (i) 0.0525   (ii) $\frac{21}{400}$
2. (a) 50%   (b) 60%   (c) 23%   (d) 35%
   (e) 85%   (f) 30%   (g) 57.5%   (h) 22.5%
   (i) 2.25%   (j) 83.3%
3.

Fraction	Decimal	Percentage
$\frac{3}{20}$	0.15	15%
$\frac{2}{25}$	0.08	8%
$\frac{7}{10}$	0.7	70%
$\frac{8}{25}$	0.32	32%
$\frac{7}{8}$	0.875	87.5%
$\frac{1}{6}$	0.1$\dot{6}$	$16\frac{2}{3}$%
$\frac{7}{40}$	0.175	17.5%

Exercise 2O

1. (a) 27   (b) 42   (c) 11   (d) 9
   (e) £1.80   (f) £9   (g) £8.75   (h) 262.5 kg
   (i) 10 g   (j) £17.91
2. (a) 78 women   (b) 72 men
3. 10.5 g   4. £4730   5. 156 pages
6. £4.50   7. £1.50

Mixed exercise 2

1. (a) $\frac{1}{2} = \frac{4}{8}$ (b) $\frac{3}{4} = \frac{12}{16}$ (c) $\frac{5}{8} = \frac{15}{24}$
2. (a) $\frac{2}{3}$ (b) $\frac{9}{11}$ (c) $\frac{3}{4}$ (d) $\frac{3}{4}$
3. (a) $\frac{7}{4}$ (b) $\frac{16}{7}$ (c) $\frac{29}{8}$
4. (a) Eat at their desk   (b) Do not eat lunch
5. $\frac{3}{10}, \frac{1}{3}, \frac{3}{5}, \frac{5}{6}$
6. (a) 3.13   (b) 43.8   (c) 0.0256
   (d) 20   (e) 0.0056   (f) 2130
7. $\frac{13}{15}$
8. (a) $1\frac{1}{24}$ (b) $\frac{11}{30}$ (c) $1\frac{7}{8}$ (d) $\frac{2}{3}$
9. 12.5 kg
10. 0.0068 kg
11. (a) 4.264   (b) 4.4   (c) 83.46   (d) 3.6
12. 15 servings
13. £79.86
14. (a) 0.8   (b) 0.875   (c) $0.\dot{5}$
15. (a) $\frac{4}{25}$ (b) $\frac{3}{5}$ (c) $\frac{97}{200}$
   (d) $\frac{5}{9}$ (e) $\frac{33}{99}$ (f) $\frac{437}{3330}$
16. (a) $3.3, 3, \frac{3}{4}, \frac{3}{8}, 0.3$ (b) $0.\dot{7}, 0.77, \frac{3}{4}, \frac{37}{50}, \frac{7}{10}$
17. (a) 19.683   (b) 14.44   (c) ±3.8   (d) 2.3
   (e) 5.51 or 3.31   (f) 14.784 (3 d.p.)
   (g) 4.745 (3 d.p.) or 0.055 (3 d.p.)
18. £31.90
19. No, it is not possible to measure 3.33 cm. 3.3 cm would be more sensible.
20.

Fraction	Decimal	Percentage
$\frac{3}{5}$	0.6	60%
$\frac{6}{25}$	0.24	24%
$\frac{13}{40}$	0.325	32.5%
$\frac{5}{6}$	$0.8\dot{3}$	$83.\dot{3}$%

21. (a) 24   (b) £2.40   (c) £6   (d) 60 g
22. (a) 68   (b) 12
23. £423
24. £72.25
25. 80%

Exercise 3A

1. (a) $\frac{1}{16}$ (b) $\frac{1}{64}$ (c) $\frac{1}{27}$ (d) $\frac{1}{16}$ (e) 6
   (f) 10   (g) 2   (h) 10   (i) $\frac{1}{5}$ (j) $\frac{1}{7}$
   (k) $\frac{1}{3}$ (l) $\frac{1}{4}$ (m) 1   (n) 1   (o) 16
   (p) 32   (q) 125   (r) $\frac{1}{100}$ (s) $\frac{1}{81}$ (t) $\frac{1}{32}$

Exercise 3B

1. (a) 8×10^2 (b) 7×10^3 (c) 9×10^4
   (d) 8.72×10^2 (e) 9.2×10^3 (f) 8.7×10^3
   (g) 9.84×10^4 (h) 8.34×10^5 (i) 1.2×10^6
2. (a) 300   (b) 50 000   (c) 8 000 000
   (d) 25 000   (e) 3 800 000   (f) 23 600
   (g) 4 780 000   (h) 294 000   (i) 38 400 000

3. (a) 8×10^{-1} (b) 7.2×10^{-1} (c) 4×10^{-2}
   (d) 2×10^{-2} (e) 5.3×10^{-3} (f) 8.9×10^{-3}
   (g) 3.2×10^{-3} (h) 4.85×10^{-2} (i) 4.1×10^{-5}
4. (a) 0.2   (b) 0.03
   (c) 0.0005   (d) 0.021
   (e) 0.000 034   (f) 0.000 58
   (g) 0.000 002 38   (h) 0.000 000 043 9
   (i) 0.000 000 026 1
5. (a) 4.56×10^5 (b) 3.4×10^{-4} (c) 1.6×10^8
6. (a) 1.15×10^5 (b) 9.4×10^{-3}
   (c) 1.53×10^7 (d) 8.2×10^{-4}

Exercise 3C

1. (a) 6.3×10^7 (b) 2.1×10^{-1} (c) 4×10^1
   (d) 3×10^3 (e) 1.65×10^3 (f) 4×10^7
2. (a) 9.50×10^9 (b) 7.38×10^{-3} (c) 1.42×10^1
   (d) 1.36×10^{-10} (e) 3.35×10^{-6} (f) 4.69×10^{10}
3. 5.36×10^{-19} grams
4. (a) 1.8144×10^{14} m   (b) 5×10^2 seconds
5. 30 times
6. 239 people per km²

Exercise 3D

1. (a) 2 800 000   (b) 2.7   (c) 3600
   (d) 0.0024   (e) 20 000   (f) 50
   (g) 2250   (h) 0.04
2. (a) 350   (b) 15   (c) 45
   (d) 100   (e) 50   (f) 60
3. (a) 400, larger   (b) $2\frac{2}{3}$, larger
   (c) 3, larger   (d) 12, larger
4. 600 min or 60 hours
5. 8000p or £80
6. 20 000p or £200
7. 160 s or 170 s
8. 504 000 s
9. (a) 0.6 mm   (b) 12 mm

Mixed exercise 3

1. (a) $\frac{1}{36}$ (b) 1   (c) $\frac{1}{8}$ (d) 7
   (e) 2   (f) 9   (g) $\frac{1}{9}$ (h) $\frac{1}{125}$
2. (a) 3×10^3 (b) 5.8×10^3 (c) 7.89×10^5
   (d) 8.63×10^4 (e) 5×10^{-1} (f) 6.1×10^{-2}
   (g) 2.1×10^{-4} (h) 3.81×10^{-4}
3. (a) 20 000   (b) 2300   (c) 384 000
   (d) 89 700 000   (e) 0.0003   (f) 0.000 002 1
   (g) 0.007 92   (h) 0.0826
4. (a) 8.04×10^4 (b) 1.528×10^{-4}
5. 480 000 minutes
6. (a) 9.4608×10^{15} m   (b) 1.356×10^5 seconds
7. 1.28×10^{13} bacteria
8. (a) 1.26×10^8 (b) 1.66×10^4
   (c) 3×10^2 (d) 5×10^1
9. $5.829 76 \times 10^{-20}$ grams
10. 1.5×10^4 seconds
11. (a) 1200   (b) 0.0036   (c) 300 000   (d) 0.2
12. 1700 times

Exercise 4A

1. (a) $5x$ (b) $4y$ (c) $6ab$ (d) $3x^2$
   (e) $5x^2y$ (f) $2pq^2$ (g) $5cd^2$ (h) $11a^2b^3$
2. (a) $5a + 4b$ (b) $6x + y$
   (c) $3p - 5q$ (d) $4a + 6ab - 3bc + abc$
   (e) $4ab^2 - a^2b$

Exercise 4B

1. $4x + 28$
2. $9x - 18$
3. $20x + 5$
4. $18x - 8$
5. $21 - 12x$
6. $x^2 + 9x$
7. $x^2 - 8x$
8. $5x^2 - 4x$
9. $2x^2 + 7x$
10. $3x - 2x^2$
11. $-2x - 10$
12. $-28x + 7$
13. $-30 + 5x$
14. $16x^2 + 56x$
15. $21x^2 - 35x$
16. $12x - 28x^2$
17. $-2x^2 - 5x$
18. $-18x^2 - 9x$
19. $-15x^2 + 12x$
20. $-16x - 6x^2$
21. $-28x + 4x^2$
22. $ax + 5a$
23. $3ax - 7a$
24. $10ax + 15a$
25. $21ax - 35a$
26. $8a^2 - 16ax$
27. $3x^2 + 8x$
28. $7x^2 - 5x$
29. $2x^3 + 9x^2$
30. $5x^3 - 4x^2$

Exercise 4C

1. $6(x + 3)$
2. $7(x - 4)$
3. $5(4x + 3)$
4. $8(2x - 3)$
5. $a(x + 8)$
6. $a(x - 5b)$
7. $7(2x^2 + 3)$
8. $9(3x^2 - 2)$
9. $x(x + 1)$
10. $x(x - 2)$
11. $8x(x - 3)$
12. $7x(5x + 3)$
13. $6x(2 - 3x)$
14. $ax(x - 4)$
15. $4ax(x + 5)$
16. $6ax(5x - 3)$
17. $ax(x - a)$
18. $4ax(3a + 2x)$
19. $5a(3 - 4x^2)$
20. $3ax(3a - 7x)$

Exercise 4D

1. $5x - 1$
2. $9x - 3$
3. $8x - 7$
4. $18x - 13$
5. $6x - 7$
6. $4x - 9$
7. $4x + 1$
8. $6 - 5x$
9. $7x - 45$
10. $6x + 29$
11. 20
12. 9
13. $-8x - 11$
14. $20 - x$
15. $4x$
16. $x + 13$
17. $x^2 + 3x - 15$
18. $x^2 - 3x + 21$
19. $3x^2 + 8x - 6$
20. $7x^2 - 10x - 10$
21. $6x^2 + 5x - 4$
22. $10x^2 - 4x - 15$
23. $5x - 5$
24. 13
25. $5x - 11$
26. $17x - 5$
27. $9x + 14$
28. $x - 20$
29. $2x + 2$
30. 0

Exercise 4E

1. (a) $x^2 + 8x + 15$ (b) $x^2 + 7x + 12$
   (c) $x^2 + 10x + 16$ (d) $x^2 + 3x - 4$
   (e) $x^2 - 3x - 18$ (f) $x^2 + 2x - 24$
   (g) $x^2 - 12x + 27$ (h) $x^2 - 3x - 40$
   (i) $x^2 - 7x + 6$ (j) $x^2 - 64$
   (k) $x^2 - 8x + 12$ (l) $x^2 - 144$
2. (a) $ab + 5a + 4b + 20$ (b) $cd - 3c + 7d - 21$
   (c) $pq - 3p - 2q + 6$ (d) $xy + 7x - 5y - 35$
   (e) $at - 9a - 4t + 36$ (f) $bc - 8b + 5c - 40$
3. (a) $x^2 + 8x + 16$ (b) $x^2 - 2x + 1$
   (c) $x^2 + 14x + 49$ (d) $x^2 - 18x + 81$
4. (a) $3x^2 - 7x - 6$ (b) $6x^2 - 17x - 14$
   (c) $8x^2 - 22x + 15$ (d) $2xy + 4x - 7y - 14$
   (e) $10x^2 - 39x + 14$ (f) $10xy - 5x + 12y - 6$
   (g) $9x^2 - 49$ (h) $12x^2 + 51x + 45$
   (i) $25x^2 - 81$ (j) $4x^2 + 12x + 9$
   (k) $9x^2 - 30x + 25$ (l) $25x^2 + 10x + 1$
   (m) $49x^2 - 28x + 4$ (n) $10x^2 + 19xy + 7y^2$
   (o) $8x^2 - 4xy - 12y^2$ (p) $14x^2 - 41xy + 15y^2$
   (q) $25x^2 - 49y^2$ (r) $16x^2 - 8xy + y^2$
   (s) $18x^2 + 17xy - 15y^2$ (t) $9x^2 + 30xy + 25y^2$
   (u) $81x^2 - 4y^2$ (v) $64x^2 - 48xy + 9y^2$
5. (a) $x^2 + 2x - 6$ (b) $4x^2 - 8$
   (c) $2x^2 - 14x + 29$ (d) 11
   (e) $2x^2 + 10x + 37$ (f) $22x + 33$
   (g) $20x$ (h) $30e + 9$
   (i) $24x - 32$ (j) $9x^2 + 16x - 14$
   (k) $25x^2 - 26x + 7$ (l) x^2

Exercise 4F

1. (a) $x(3x + 5)$ (b) $3(3x^2 - 4)$ (c) $x(x - 2)$
   (d) $7(3x^2 + 1)$ (e) $a(x^2 - 5)$ (f) $x(bx + 3)$
   (g) $7(x^2 - 4py)$ (h) $x(ax + b)$ (i) $2(3x^2 - 4y)$
   (j) $a(x^2 + y)$ (k) $4(2ax^2 - by)$ (l) $x(1 - 5x)$
2. (a) $5x(x + 2)$ (b) $3x(3x - 2)$ (c) $4x(3x - 1)$
   (d) $5x(3x + 2)$ (e) $ax(x - 4)$ (f) $3x(x + 2b)$
   (g) $cx(x - 2)$ (h) $ax(x + 1)$ (i) $xy(x + y)$
   (j) $4y(3xy - 2)$ (k) $4x(2x + 3y)$ (l) $xy(2xy - 5)$
   (m) $3xy(2x + 5)$ (n) $2xy(5y - 4x)$ (o) $3bx(2x + 1)$
3. (a) $(x + 1)(x + 3)$ (b) $(x - 3)(x + 1)$
   (c) $(x - 2)(x - 1)$ (d) $(x - 7)(x + 1)$
   (e) $(x - 5)(x - 1)$ (f) $(x + 1)(x + 11)$
   (g) $(x + 1)^2$ (h) $(x - 11)(x + 1)$
   (i) $(x - 4)^2$ (j) $(x - 6)(x - 1)$
   (k) $(x - 5)(x - 4)$ (l) $(x - 5)(x + 4)$
   (m) $(x + 3)^2$ (n) $(x - 10)^2$
   (o) $(x - 2)(x + 5)$ (p) $(x - 12)(x + 1)$
   (q) $(x + 3)(x + 5)$ (r) $(x - 7)(x - 2)$
   (s) $(x - 5)(x + 6)$ (t) $(x + 5)^2$
   (u) $(x - 7)(x + 4)$
4. (a) $(x - 1)(3x - 1)$ (b) $(x + 3)(2x - 1)$
   (c) $3(x - 7)(x + 1)$ (d) $(5x - 7)(x - 1)$
   (e) $(3x + 2)^2$ (f) $7(x - 3)(x - 2)$
   (g) $(2x + 5)(4x - 1)$ (h) $(x + 6)(5x - 2)$
   (i) $4(x - 5)^2$ (j) $(3x - 4)^2$
   (k) $(2x + 1)(3x - 8)$ (l) $3(x - 1)(2x + 5)$
   (m) $(3x - 2)(4x - 5)$ (n) $5(2x - 3)^2$
   (o) $(3x + 4)(5x - 3)$ (p) $(2x - 3)(7x + 6)$
   (q) $(2x - 1)(10x + 21)$ (r) $4(2x - 1)(3x - 2)$

Exercise 4G

1. (a) $(x + 2)(x - 2)$ (b) $(x + 4)(x - 4)$
   (c) $(x + 1)(x - 1)$ (d) $(x + 10)(x - 10)$
   (e) $(x + 8)(x - 8)$ (f) $(x + 12)(x - 12)$
2. (a) $5(x + 3)(x - 3)$ (b) $2(x + 6)(x - 6)$
   (c) $4(x + 5)(x - 5)$ (d) $7(x + 1)(x - 1)$
   (e) $3(x + 4)(x - 4)$ (f) $6(x + 2)(x - 2)$
3. (a) $(3x + 4)(3x - 4)$ (b) $(7x + 3)(7x - 3)$
   (c) $(9x + 8)(9x - 8)$

Exercise 4H

1. (a) $x + 3$ (b) $3x - 2$ (c) $4(2x + 3)$
   (d) $2(3x - 2)$ (e) $3 - 2x$ (f) $2(3 - 5x)$
   (g) $2x + 5y$ (h) $2(3x - y)$ (i) $2(x + 2y)$
   (j) $2x - 3y$ (k) $2(4x + 3y)$ (l) $2(x - 2y)$
2. (a) $x + 5$ (b) $3x - 4$ (c) $1 - 2x$
   (d) $4(x - 3)$ (e) $7(x + 1)$ (f) $2(3x - 7)$
   (g) $5(x - 2)$ (h) $5(x + 4)$ (i) $3(2x - 1)$
   (j) $4(2x + 3)$ (k) $4(5 - 4x)$ (l) $\frac{3}{2}(4 - 5x)$

Exercise 4I

1. x

2. $\dfrac{26}{7x}$

3. $\dfrac{8x + 14}{15}$

4. $\dfrac{7x + 10}{(x + 1)(x + 2)}$

5. $\dfrac{2(2 - y)}{y(4 - y)}$

6. $\dfrac{2y + 17}{4(2y - 3)}$

7. $\dfrac{3x^2 + 8x + 1}{(x - 1)(x + 1)^2}$

8. $\dfrac{2(x - 3)}{x^2(x - 2)}$

Exercise 4J

1 $\dfrac{3(x-4)}{x+2}$ 2 $\dfrac{2(x+1)}{x-5}$ 3 $\dfrac{x+3}{x-2}$

4 $\dfrac{7x}{x+4}$ 5 $\dfrac{x+1}{x-1}$ 6 $\dfrac{x-1}{4}$

7 $\dfrac{2(x+4)}{x+1}$ 8 $\dfrac{x-5}{x+6}$ 9 $5(x-6)$

10 $\dfrac{3(x-1)}{4}$ 11 3 12 $\dfrac{x}{x+7}$

13 $\dfrac{x+4}{5x}$ 14 $\dfrac{2x(x+5)}{5(x-1)}$ 15 $\dfrac{x+8}{x+1}$

16 $2(x-5)$

Mixed exercise 4

1 (a) $8x+40$ (b) $21x-28$
  (c) $5-30x$ (d) $9x^2-2x$
  (e) $-8x-20$ (f) $6x^2-18x$
  (g) $-10x^2+14x$ (h) $8ax+3a^2$
  (i) $9x-4x^2$

2 (a) $9(x-3)$ (b) $7(4x+3)$
  (c) $10(x^2-2)$ (d) $x(x-1)$
  (e) $8x(4x+5)$ (f) $8x(3+2x)$
  (g) $x(ax-b)$ (h) $3ax(2x-3)$
  (i) $5ax(5-3x)$

3 (a) $12x-15$ (b) $5(y+8)$
  (c) $12a+11b$

4 (a) x^{-5} (b) $12w^8y^6$

5 (a) $9x-22$ (b) $27x-2$
  (c) $5x-11$ (d) $8x+5$
  (e) $19-15x$ (f) $10-4x$
  (g) x^2+5x+8 (h) $9-2x$

6 (a) $x^2+11x+18$ (b) x^2+6x-7
  (c) $x^2-10x+16$ (d) $x^2+2x-15$
  (e) x^2-9 (f) $x^2-8x+16$
  (g) $x^2+16x+64$ (h) $2x^2-9x-35$
  (i) $8x^2-14x+3$ (j) $9x^2-1$
  (k) $9x^2-6x+1$ (l) $16x^2+56x+49$
  (m) $10x^2-xy-2y^2$ (n) $25x^2-40xy+16y^2$
  (o) $9x^2-16y^2$

7 (a) $3a(4a-3)$ (b) $ab(b-7)$
  (c) $5a(3b^2+4)$ (d) $2c(3c+1)$
  (e) $pq(3q-2)$ (f) $6xy(4y+3x)$

8 (a) $(x+9)(x-9)$ (b) $5(x+2)(x-2)$
  (c) $8(x+2)(x-2)$ (d) $9(x+1)(x-1)$

9 (a) $x(x+3)$ (b) k^3
  (c) (i) $7x-1$ (ii) $2x+5y$
  (d) $(p+q)(p+q+5)$

10 (a) $5x+3$ (b) $2x-5$
  (c) $7x+4y$ (d) $x-2$
  (e) $5(x+8)$ (f) $9(3x-8)$

11 (a) $(x+1)(x+7)$ (b) $(x+2)(x-1)$
  (c) $(x-4)(x-3)$ (d) $(x-8)(x+8)$
  (e) $(x-9)(x+2)$ (f) $(x-9)^2$
  (g) $3(x-6)(x+6)$ (h) $(x-5)(3x-4)$
  (i) $(4x-1)(4x+1)$ (j) $(3x-4)(4x+1)$
  (k) $(2x-7)^2$ (l) $(4x+1)(5x-8)$

12 (a) a^7 (b) $15x^3y^4$
  (c) $x-1$ (d) $(a-3b)(a+3b)$

13 (a) $\dfrac{8x}{x+4}$ (b) $\dfrac{x-3)}{5(x+3)}$

  (c) $\dfrac{(x+2)}{x-1}$ (d) $\dfrac{x-2}{x+1}$

  (e) $\dfrac{2(x-3)}{15(x+2)(x+3)}$ (f) $\dfrac{2x-3}{(x+3)(x-3)}$

  (g) $\dfrac{2}{x-5}$ (h) $\dfrac{x+4}{x}$

  (i) $\dfrac{4(x+1)}{3(x+7)}$ (j) $\dfrac{(x-10)(x-2)}{(x+1)(x+10)}$

Exercise 5A

1 A $(-2, 3)$ E $(0, -4)$ H $(-5, -3)$
  B $(5, -1)$ F $(6, 2)$ I $(-3, -4)$
  C $(-5, 0)$ G $(-6, 4)$ J $(3, -2)$
  D $(-2, -2)$

2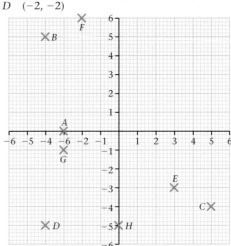

Exercise 5B

1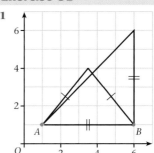

There are many other possibilities for each triangle.

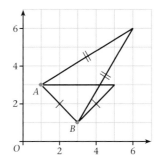

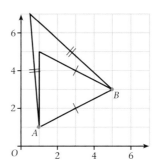

2

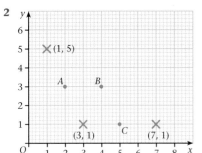

(1, 5), (7, 1)
or (3, 1)

3

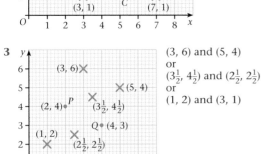

(3, 6) and (5, 4)
or
$(3\frac{1}{2}, 4\frac{1}{2})$ and $(2\frac{1}{2}, 2\frac{1}{2})$
or
(1, 2) and (3, 1)

4

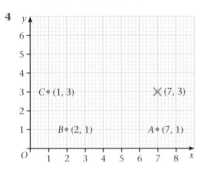

(7, 3) is one
example of *D*
that will make
a trapezium.

Exercise 5C

1 (a) (i) (7, 1) (ii) (0, 3) (iii) (7, 5)
(b) (14, 3)
(c) (i) (7, 3) (ii) (10.5, 4)
(d) *x* = 7

2 (a)

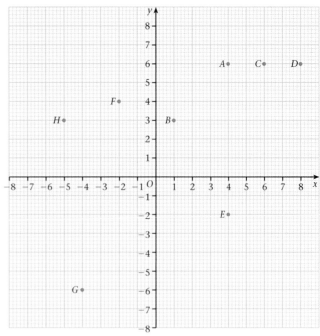

(b) mid-points: *AC*(5, 6), *AE*(4, 2), *EF*(1, 1),
FH(−3.5, 3.5), *EG*(0, −4), *FH*(−3.5, 3.5), *BH*(−2, 3)

3 (a) (−0.5, 0.5)
(b) (0.5, −0.5)

4 (8, 11)

5

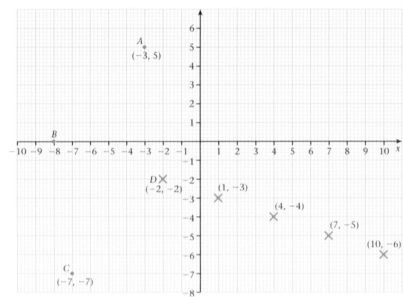

(a) *D*(−2, −2)
(b) For a kite the points could be:
(1, −3) (4, −4) (7, −5) (10, −6)

Exercise 5D

1

Two-dimensional	Three-dimensional
pentagon	pyramid
hexagon	cylinder
triangle	cone
trapezium	cuboid
rectangle	sphere
square	
circle	

2 (1, 4, 2), (6.2, 1, 4), (2, 3, 4), (4, 5, 0), (6, 0, 7), (−3, 0, 0)

3 $P(2, 2, −1)$, $Q(−1, −1, 3)$, $R(2, −1, 3)$, $S(2, −1, −1)$, $T(−1, 2, −1)$, $U(−1, 2, 3)$, $V(2, 2, 3)$, $W(−1, −1, −1)$

Exercise 5E

1 A $y = −1$
B $x = 4$
C $x = −3$
D $y = 2$

2
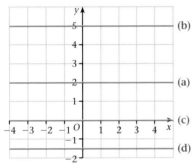

The lines are all horizontal and parallel.

Exercise 5F

1 (a) (b)
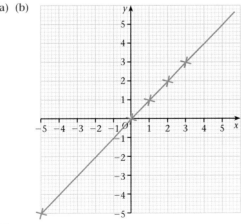
(c) $y = x$

2 $y = −x$

3
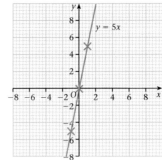

4 (a) They all go through the origin and lie in the 1st and 3rd quadrants.
(b) They all go through the origin and lie in the 2nd and 4th quadrants.

5 (a) (b)
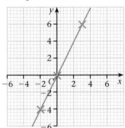
(c) $y = 2x$

6 (a) (b)
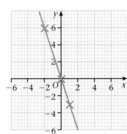
(c) $y = −3x$

Exercise 5G

1

x	−3	−2	−1	0	1	2	3
y	−11	−8	−5	−2	1	4	7

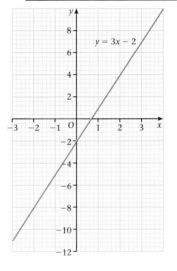

2

x	−6	−4	−2	0	2	4	6
y	−1	0	1	2	3	4	5

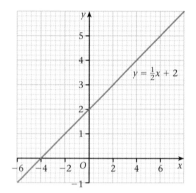

$y = \frac{1}{2}x + 2$

5

x	−4	−2	0	2	4	6	8	10
y	5	4	3	2	1	0	−1	−2

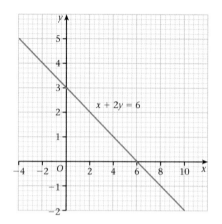

$x + 2y = 6$

3

x	−2	−1	0	1	2	3	4	5	6
y	7	6	5	4	3	2	1	0	−1

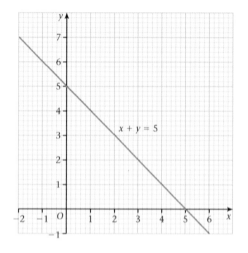

$x + y = 5$

6

x	−4	0	4	8	12
y	6	3	0	−3	−6

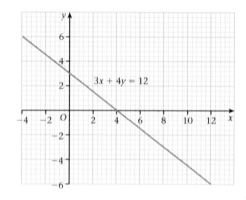

$3x + 4y = 12$

4

x	−2	−1	0	1	2	3	4	5	6
y	−3	−2	−1	0	1	2	3	4	5

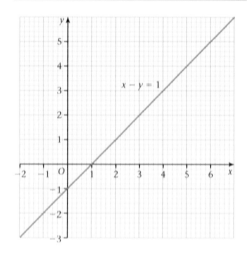

$x - y = 1$

7

x	−3	0	3	6	9	12
y	−8	−6	−4	−2	0	2

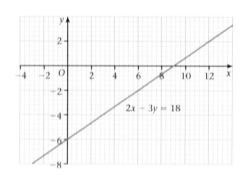

$2x - 3y = 18$

8

x	−8	−4	0	4	8
y	7	4	1	−2	−5

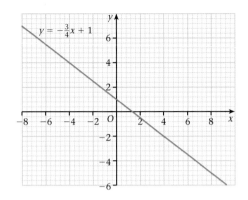

(d)

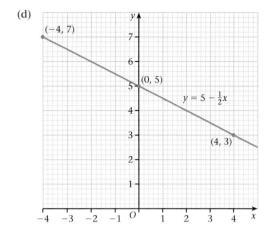

9 (a)

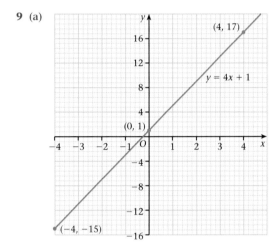

(e)

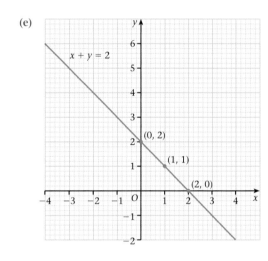

(b)

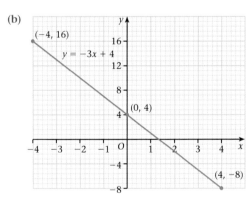

(f)

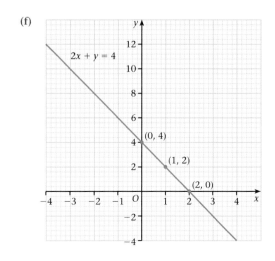

(c)

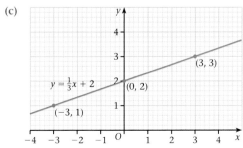

(g)

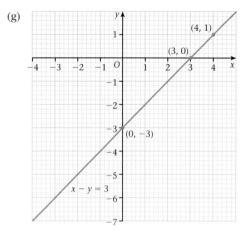

(h)

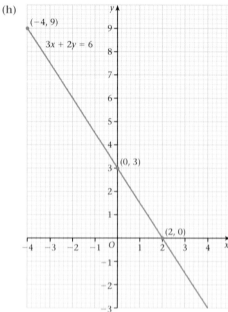

(i)

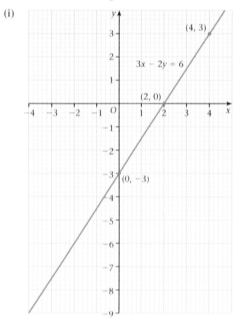

10 (a) (0, 1)   (b) (0, 4)   (c) (0, 2)
   (d) (0, 5)   (e) (0, 2)   (f) (0, 4)
   (g) (0, −3) (h) (0, 3)   (i) (0, −3)
   Lines (g) and (i) both cross the y-axis below the x-axis.
   All the others cross the y-axis above the x-axis.

Mixed exercise 5

1 (a)

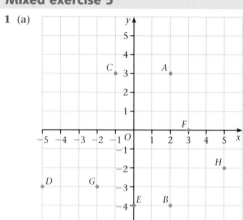

  (b) mid-points BE(1, −4), AG(0, 0), AC(0.5, 3),
     DG(−3.5, −3), EH(2.5, −3), CD(−3, 0),
     GH(1.5, −2.5), CE(−0.5, −0.5)

2 (5, 1), (7, 5), (−3, 7)

3 (0, 1), (2, 7)

4 (a) 1-D   (b) 2-D   (c) 2-D
   (d) 1-D   (e) 3-D   (f) 2-D
   (g) 3-D   (h) 3-D   (i) 1-D
   (j) 2-D

5

x	−3	−2	−1	0	1	2	3
y	−7	−3	1	5	9	13	17

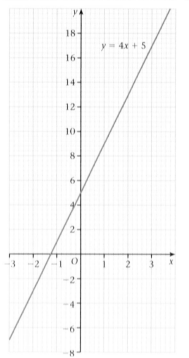

6 (a)

x	-2	-1	0	1	2	3
y	-1	1	3	5	7	9

(b)

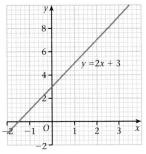

(c) (i) $y = 0.4$
(ii) $x = 1.2$

7

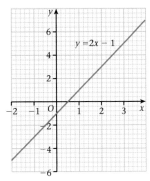

8 (a)

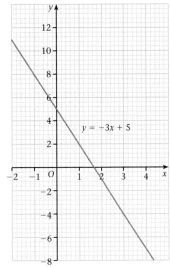

(b) Another way of writing $y = 3x + 5$ is $3x + y = 5$

9

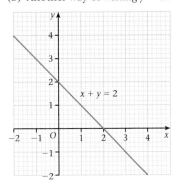

10

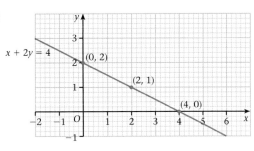

11

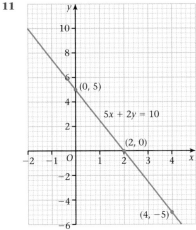

Exercise 6A

1 (i) 4, 6, 8, ... even numbers
(ii) 10, 15, 20, ... multiples of 5
(iii) 4, 8, 16, ... powers of 2
2 (a) 15, 11, 7, ...
(b) 25, 5, 1, ...
(c) 7, 31, 127, ...
(d) 8, 12, 28, ...
(e) 32, 20, 14, ...
3 (a) add 6; 37, 43, ...
(b) subtract 7; 8, 1, ...
(c) multiply by 5; 1250, 6250, ...
(d) divide by 2; 4, 2, ...
4 (a) 54, 63, ...; multiples of 9
(b) 100 000, 1 000 000... powers of 10
5 (a) subtract 6 5, -1, ...
(b) divide by 10 $1, \frac{1}{10},$ ...
(c) add 3 $-1, 2,$ ...
(d) divide by 4 $\frac{1}{4}, \frac{1}{16},$ ...
6 (a) 35 (b) 67 (c) 68 (d) 72
7 (a) 3, 5, 7, 9, ...
(b) Each difference is 2 more than the previous difference.
(c) 36, 49, 64, 81, 100, ...
8 (a) 2, 3, 4, 5, ...
(b) Each difference is 1 more than the previous difference.
(c) 21, 28, 36, 45, 55, ...

Exercise 6B

1 (a) (i) 6, 12, 18, 24, 30 (ii) 72
(b) (i) 5, 8, 11, 14, 17 (ii) 38
(c) (i) 4, 11, 18, 25, 32 (ii) 81
(d) (i) 27, 22, 17, 12, 7 (ii) -28
(e) (i) 16, 8, 0, -8, -16 (ii) -72

2 (a) $7n$ (b) $6n + 5$ (c) $n + 6$
   (d) $27 - 4n$ (e) $8n - 3$ (f) $13 - n$
   (g) $41 - 10n$ (h) $7n - 21$
3 (a) $2n$ (b) $2n - 1$ (c) $8n$
   (d) $2n + 8$ (e) $2n + 13$ (f) $5n + 30$

Exercise 6C

1 (a) (i) Shape number 5 has 11 matchsticks, shape number 6 has 13 matchsticks
     (ii) $2n + 1$ (iii) 61   (iv) Shape number 105
   (b) (i) Shape number 5 has 16 matchsticks, shape number 6 has 19 matchsticks
     (ii) $3n + 1$ (iii) 91   (iv) Shape number 70
   (c) (i) Shape number 5 has 26 matchsticks, shape number 6 has 31 matchsticks
     (ii) $5n + 1$ (iii) 151   (iv) Shape number 42
   (d) (i) Shape number 5 has 36 matchsticks, shape number 6 has 43 matchsticks
     (ii) $7n + 1$ (iii) 211   (iv) Shape number 30
2 (a) The coefficient is one less than the number of matchsticks in shape number 1. This is becuase to produce the next shape in the sequence the number of matchsticks we add is one less than the number in shape number 1.
   (b) $19n + 1$
3 (a) Pattern number 5 has 16 tiles, pattern number 6 has 18 tiles.
   (b) $2n + 6$
   (c) 40 tiles
   (d) Pattern number 32
4 (a) Pattern number 5 has 17 dots, pattern number 6 has 20 dots
   (b) $3n + 2$
   (c) 89 dots
   (d) Pattern number 36
5 (a) Pattern number 5 has 17 tiles, pattern number 6 has 21 tiles
   (b) $4n - 3$
   (c) 97 tiles
   (d) Pattern number 23
   (e) Pattern number 15
6 (a) Pattern number 5 has 16 tiles, pattern number 6 has 19 tiles
   (b) $3n + 1$
   (c) 85 tiles
   (d) Pattern number 43
   (e) Pattern number 26

Mixed exercise 6

1 (a) 20, 27, 34, ...   (b) 12, 48, 192, ...
   (c) 24, 119, 594, ...   (d) 12, 14, 18, ...
2 (a) 23   (b) 31
3 (a) (i) Each term is 8 more than the previous term
     (ii) 43, 51
   (b) (i) Each term is $\frac{1}{2} \times$ the previous term
     (ii) $\frac{1}{4}, \frac{1}{8}$
   (c) (i) Each term is 4 less than the previous term
     (ii) 0, -4
   (d) (i) Each difference is 2 times the previous one
     (ii) 127, 255
4 (a) (i) 12, 19, 26, 33, 40
     (ii) 75
     (iii) $7n + 5$
   (b) (i) 1, 10, 19, 28, 37
     (ii) 82
     (iii) $9n - 8$
   (c) (i) 15, 10, 5, 0, -5
     (ii) -30
     (iii) $20 - 5n$

5 (a) (i) 2, 11, 20, 29, 38   (ii) 173
   (b) (i) 11, 19, 27, 35, 43   (ii) 163
   (c) (i) 34, 28, 22, 16, 10   (ii) -80
   (d) (i) 21, 24, 27, 210, 213   (ii) -58
6 (a) $7n - 4$ (b) $23 - 3n$ (c) $8n + 5$ (d) $10 - 5n$
7 (a) 28, 33
   (b) Each term is 5 more than the previous term.
   (c) Terms all end in 3 or 8 so 387 is not a term.
8 (a) $7n - 3$
   (b) $7 \times 100 - 3 = 697$. Jane is correct.
9 (a)

   (b) Pattern number 4, 22 dots
     Pattern number 5, 26 dots
   (c) 46 dots
   (d) $d = 4n + 6$
10 (a) Shape number 5 has 26 matchsticks, shape number 6 has 31 matchsticks
   (b) $5n + 1$
   (c) 116 matchsticks
   (d) Shape number 11
   (e) Shape number 39
11 (a) Pattern number 5 has 21 tiles, pattern number 6 has 25 tiles
   (b) $3n + 1$
   (c) $4n + 1$
   (d) 37 octagonal tiles
   (e) 101 tiles in total
   (f) 40 octagonal tiles
   (g) 77 tiles in total

Exercise 7A

1 pentagon   **2** hexagon
3 quadrilateral   **4** triangle
5 nonagon   **6** heptagon

Exercise 7B

1 right-angled scalene triangle
2 equilateral triangle
3 isosceles triangle
4 isosceles triangle
5 right-angled scalene triangle
6 isosceles triangle
7 equilateral triangle
8 obtuse scalene triangle

Exercise 7C

1 $a = 30°$ **2** $b = 27°$
3 $c = 37°$ **4** $d = 119°$
5 $e = 63°, f = 54°$ **6** $g = 34°$
7 $h = 45°$ **8** $i = 82°$
9 $j = 66°, k = 48°$ **10** $l = 54°, m = 63°$
11 (a) $a = 48°$ (b) $x = 20°$ (c) $b = 30°$
   (d) $y = 25°$ (e) $x = 18°$

Exercise 7D

1 trapezium   **2** square
3 rectangle   **4** parallelogram
5 square   **6** kite
7 trapezium   **8** parallelogram
9 arrowhead   **10** trapezium

11 (a) rectangle, square
   (b) parallelogram, rhombus, rectangle, square
   (c) arrowhead
   (d) parallelogram, rhombus, rectangle, square
   (e) kite, arrowhead

12 (a)

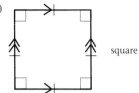

square

(b)

parallelogram

(c)

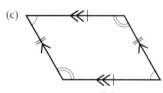

parallelogram

(d)

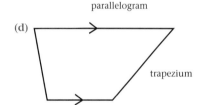

trapezium

Exercise 7E

1 $a = 46°$ (corresponding angles (parallel lines))
2 $b = 53°$ (alternate angles (parallel lines))
3 $a = 112°$ (alternate angles (parallel lines))
4 $b = 180° - 50° = 130°$ (angles on a straight line, alternate angles)
   $d = 115°$ (corresponding angles)
   $c = 180° - 115° = 65°$ (angles on a straight line)
5 $e = 57°$ (alternate angles)
   $f = 57°$ (vertically opposite angles)
6 $b = 55°$ (opposite angles of parallelogram)
   $a = c = \frac{1}{2}(360° - 110°) = 125°$ (angle sum of quadrilateral, opposite angles of parallelogram)
7 $c = 127°$ (corresponding angles (parallel lines), vertically opposite angles)
8 $d = 102°$ (vertically opposite angles, corresponding angles, base angles of an isosceles triangle, angles of a triangle add up to 180°)
9 $e = 20.5°$ (base angles of an isosceles triangle, vertically opposite angles)
10 $f + 25° + 60° = 180°$
   $f = 95°$ (vertically opposite angles, angles of a triangle add up to 180°)
   $g = 120°$ (angles on a straight line, corresponding angles)
11 $h = 44°$ (corresponding angles, angles on a straight line)
   $j = 74°$ (angles of a triangle add up to 180°, angles on a straight line)
12 $k = 47°$ (alternate angles)
   $m = 99°$ (angles of a triangle add up to 180°)
   $n = 81°$ (alternate angles, angles on a straight line)

Exercise 7F

1 The three angles are equal. Call each angle x.
   $3x = 180°$ (angle sum of triangle)
   $x = 60°$
2 The third angle is 70° (base angles of isosceles triangle)
   $70° + 70° + x = 180°$ (angle sum of triangle)
   $x = 40°$
3

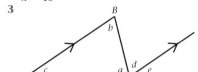

   $d = b$ (alternate angles)
   $e = c$ (corresponding angles)
   $a + d + c = 180°$ (angles on a straight line)
   so $a + b + c = 180°$
4

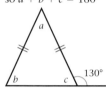

   $c = 50°$ (angles on a straight line)
   $b = c$ (base angles of isosceles triangle)
   $a + b + c = 180°$ (angle sum of triangle)
   $a + 50° + 50° = 180°$
   $a = 80°$
5

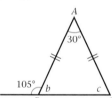

   $b + 105° = 180°$ (angles on a straight line)
   $b = 75°$
   $c + 75° + 30° = 180°$ (angle sum of triangle)
   $c = 75°$
   so $b = c$ and ABC is isosceles
6

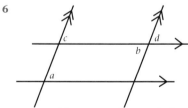

   $a = c = d$ (corresponding angles)
   $a = b$ (vertically opposite angles)
   So $a = b$

Exercise 7G

1 (a) N   (b) N

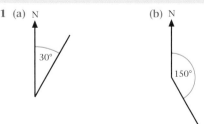

(c)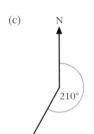

(d)
N

N
300°

2 (a) 062°   (b) 298°   (c) 118°
3 255°
4 065°
5 (i) N

(ii)

Bearing of Y from X
is $180° + b°$

Bearing of Y from X
is $180° - b°$

Mixed exercise 7

1 $a = 45°$ **2** $b = 20°$ **3** $c = 20°$
4 $d = 50°$ **5** $e = 18°$
6 $\angle ADB = 30°$
7 $a = 66°$ (corresponding angles)
8 (a) $\angle XBA = 10°$
  (b) $\angle CBE = 180° - 50° - 80° = 50°$ so $\angle CBE = \angle BCE$
    which means triangle CEB is isosceles
9 (a) $x = 109°$
  (b) corresponding angles, angles in a triangle, angles
    on a straight line
10 $a = 63°$ (corresponding angles, angles on a straight line)
11 $e = 25.5°$ (base angles of isosceles triangle, angles on a
    straight line)
    $f = 154.5°$ (base angles of isosceles triangle, angles on a
    straight line)
12 $\angle BCF = 140°$ (angles on a straight line)
    $\angle CBG = 140°$ (angles at top of regular trapezium equal)
    $\angle ABC = 40°$ (angles on a straight line)
    $\angle ACB = 40°$ (angles on a straight line)
    So $\angle ABC$ is isosceles
    $\angle BAC = 180° - 40° - 40° = 100°$
13 081°

Exercise 8A

1
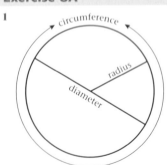

2
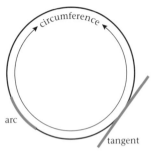

3
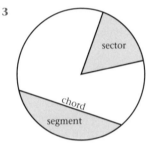

Exercise 8B

1 $A\hat{C}B + 63° = 90°$ (tangent perpendicular to radius)
   so $A\hat{C}B = 27$
2 (a) $x = 32°$ (sum of angles in triangle $= 180°$)
  (b) $y = 58°$ (tangent perpendicular to radius)
3 (a) $Q\hat{P}T = 69°$
  (b) $O\hat{P}Q = 21°$
4 (a) $A\hat{T}B = 46°$ (ATB isosceles, sum of angles in triangle
    $= 180°$)
  (b) $O\hat{B}A = 23°$ (tangent perpendicular to radius)
5 (a) $P\hat{Q}T = 63°$
  (b) $O\hat{P}Q = 27°$
6 (a) $a = 62°$ (MNT is isosceles, sum of angles in triangle
    $= 180°$)
  (b) $b = 31°$ (tangent perpendicular to radius)
7 (a) $a = 39°$ (tangent perpendicular to radius)
  (b) $b = 51°$ (sum of angles in triangle $= 180°$)

Exercise 9A

1 600 000 cm³ or 0.6 m³
2 4.99 g (3 s.f.)
3 2652.6 revolutions
4 56 500 g (3 s.f.)
5 9.42 l (3 s.f.)
6 134 sheets are needed, so 13.4 booklets

Exercise 9B

1 (a) 15.4 lb   (b) 1.32 lb
  (c) 1.36 kg   (d) 43.9 kg
  (e) 0.454 kg
2 80.9 kg
3 44.8 kg
4 26 full bottles
5 £4.43 per gallon
6 2875 g
7 167.5 cm
8 162 litres
9 11.2 gallons

Exercise 9C

1. (a) Minimum = 71.5 cm
   Maximum = 72.5 cm
   (b) Minimum = 15.5 mm
   Maximum = 16.5 mm
   (c) Minimum = 4.5 km
   Maximum = 5.5 km
   (d) Minimum = 99.5 m
   Maximum = 100.5 m
2. (a) Minimum = 49.5 kg
   Maximum = 50.5 kg
   (b) Minimum = 124.5 g
   Maximum = 125.5 g
   (c) Minimum = 2.5 tonnes
   Maximum = 3.5 tonnes
   (d) Minimum = 81.5 mg
   Maximum = 82.5 mg
3. (a) Minimum = 3.5 h
   Maximum = 4.5 h
   (b) Minimum = 22.5 min
   Maximum = 23.5 min
   (c) Minimum = 6.5 seconds
   Maximum = 7.5 seconds
   (d) Minimum = 64.5 years
   Maximum = 65.5 years
4. (a) Minimum = 25.5 °C
   Maximum = 26.5 °C
   (b) Minimum = 54.5 °F
   Maximum = 55.5 °F
   (c) Minimum = 749.5 ml
   Maximum = 750.5 ml
   (d) Minimum = 7.5 litres
   Maximum = 8.5 litres
5. (a) Minimum = 259.5 cm
   Maximum = 260.5 cm
   (b) Minimum = 5.275 m
   Maximum = 5.285 m
   (c) Minimum = 595 mm
   Maximum = 605 mm
   (d) Minimum = 1995 mm
   Maximum = 2005 mm
6. (a) $\frac{1}{2}$ hour   (b) 5 g   (c) 7.5 minutes
   (d) $\frac{1}{2}$ second   (e) 25 cm   (f) 0.1 seconds
   (g) 12.5 ml   (h) 2.5 °C

Exercise 9D

1.

	Distance	Time	Average speed
(a)	128 km	2 h	64 km/h
(b)	58 miles	$7\frac{1}{2}$ h	8 mph
(c)	600 m	20 s	30 m/s
(d)	2.3 km	50 s	46 m/s
(e)	175 miles	$3\frac{1}{2}$ h	50 mph
(f)	165 km	$2\frac{1}{2}$ h	66 km/h
(g)	750 m	30 s	25 m/s
(h)	6 km	$2\frac{1}{2}$ min	40 m/s
(i)	100 km	50 min	120 km/h
(j)	254 miles	1 h 15 min	203.2 mph
(k)	76 km	5 h 4 min	15 km/h
(l)	27.15 km	16 mins 10 s	101 km/h
(m)	127 miles	2 h 18 min 33 s	55 mph
(n)	99 miles	3 h 18 min	30 mph
(o)	2350 km	$1\frac{1}{2}$ days	65.3 km/h

2. 208 miles
3. 92.5 mph
4. 10.8 m/s (3 s.f.)
5. 3 h 27 min 16 s (nearest second)
6. 1260 m or 1.26 km
7. 11.1 km or 11 000 m
8. 4 h 37 min 30 s
9. 9 h 3 min 15 s (nearest second)
10. 217 km/h (3 s.f.)
11. 50 km/h
12. 45 km
13. 771 km/h (3 s.f.)
14. 108 km
15. (a) 82.7 m s⁻¹ (3 s.f.)
    (b) 298 km per hour (3 s.f.)
16. 266.5 m apart (4 s.f.)

Exercise 9E

1. 647 cm³ (3 s.f.)
2. 1.81 g per cm³
3. 91.44 g
4.

Substance	Mass	Volume	Density
Hydrogen	900 000 tonnes	1 km³	0.0009 g/cm³
Air	20 kg	15.38 m³	0.0013 g/cm³
Copper	14.7 kg	164 cm³	89.6 g/cm³

5. Density of dish = 11.7 g/cm³, so it is unlikely that the dish is solid silver.
6. 0.17 cm³ (2 d.p.)

Exercise 9F

1. 108 km/h
2. 26.7 m/s
3. 2 miles/minute
4. 30 mph
5. 240 km/h
6. 1 350 000 mph
7. 53.3 m/s
8. 14.2 km/litre
9. 112.5 miles/gallon
10. 1089 p/kg
11. 1.78 km/litre
12. 0.23 lb/cubic foot
13. 4 m²/litre
14. 16 000 gallons/hour
15. 4.2 litres/second

Exercise 9G

1. 10 000 kg
2. 5000 g
3. 5000 bricks
4. 8 tonnes

Exercise 9H

1. Car B
2. 3 for £1.19 (£0.397 each)
3. The litre bottle is better value (13.5p/100 ml compared with 13.6p/100 ml for the can).
4. small £2.70, medium £2.75, large £2.65
   The larger jar is best buy.
5. The water (1 g/cm³ compared to 0.8 g/cm³ for the oil)
6. Platinum (21.4 g/cm³ compared to 19.3 g/cm³ for gold)
7. James' average speed (51.2 km/h) is faster than Nitin's (50 km/h)
8. £4.20 per gallon
9. (a) The InterCity train is faster (53.3̇ m/s)
   (b) 2000 m or 2 km

Mixed exercise 9

1. 272 km
2. 112.5 litres
3. 25.5 kg (3 s.f.)
4. 400.5 m, 399.5 m
5. 3 hours 12 minutes
6. 8.33 m/s (3 s.f.)
7. 12.1 mph (3 s.f.)
8. 465 g
9. 87.4 cm³
10. (a) 8960 kg/m³   (b) 35 650 kg
11. 5.175 mph
12. 13.2 m/s
13. The 1 kg box
14. The horse rider   (b) 1 minute
15. Brian (7.9 km/h)
16. 50 kg

Exercise 10A

1. BC = 37 cm
2. (a) 96 cm²   (b) 34.72 cm²   (c) 16 cm²
3. (a) x = 6 cm   (b) x = 5 cm   (c) x = 4.5 cm

4 (a) 30 cm²   (b) 7.9 cm²   (c) 13.2 cm²
    (d) 12 cm²   (e) 84 cm²
5 (a) 36 cm²   (b) 32.5 m²   (c) 34 cm²

Exercise 10B

1 11 250 cm³ or 11.25 litres
2 15 185 cm³ or 15.2 litres (3 s.f.)
3 89 573 cm³ or 89.6 litres (3 s.f.)
4 258.19 m³ (2 d.p.)
5 3120 cm³ (3 s.f.)
6 525 cm³
7

	Length	Width	Height	Volume
(a)	4 cm	5 cm	4 cm	80 cm³
(b)	12 cm	6 cm	3 cm	216 cm³
(c)	1.6 m	10 cm	4 cm	6400 cm³
(d)	15 cm	5 mm	20 mm	15 cm³
(e)	4 m	15 cm	2.2 m	1.32 cm³
(f)	7 cm	2.5 cm	6 mm	10.5 cm³
(g)	2.4 m	15 mm	5 cm	0.0018 cm³
(h)	3 m	75 mm	3 cm	6750 cm³

8 4 cm
9 112 cm²
10

Size	Volume	Area
1, 1, 13	13	54
1, 2, 12	24	76
2, 2, 11	44	96
1, 3, 11	33	94
2, 3, 10	60	112
1, 4, 10	40	108
3, 3, 9	81	126
2, 4, 9	72	124
1, 5, 9	45	118
1, 5, 9	45	118
3, 4, 8	96	136
2, 5, 8	80	132
1, 6, 8	48	124
4, 4, 7	112	144
3, 5, 7	105	142
2, 6, 7	84	136
1, 7, 7	49	126
4, 5, 6	120	148

(a) Maximum volume when edges are 5 cm, 5 cm, 5 cm
(b) Maximum surface area when edges are 5 cm, 5 cm, 5 cm

Exercise 10C

1 1000 boxes
2 250 matchboxes
3 60 cereal packets

4 (a) 40
    (b) 192
    (c) 960
5 90 DVDs
6 100 mobile phones
7 50 matchboxes
8 360 bricks

Exercise 10D

1 Surface area = 54 cm²
2 Surface area = 1044 cm²
3 Surface area = 246 cm²
4 Surface area = 99 cm²
5 Surface area = 85 cm²
6 Surface area = 444 cm²

Exercise 10E

1 (a) 45 cm³   (b) 12 500 cm³
2 (a) (i) 540 cm³   (ii) 432 cm²
    (b) (i) 357 cm³   (ii) 386.6 cm²
    (c) (i) 540 cm³   (ii) 468 cm²
    (d) (i) 432 cm³   (ii) 380 cm²
3 19.74 m³
4 26 cm
5 (a) 739 760 cm³   (b) 10 080 cm³
    (c) 12 000 cm³   (d) 260 m³
6 (a) 216 cm³   (b) 216 cm²
7 (a) 120 cm³   (b) 168 cm²
8 (a) 216 cm³   (b) 348 cm²
9 (a) 1063.962 cm³   (b) 686.82 cm²
10 (a) 371.28 cm³   (b) 362.76 cm²
11 (a) 1.6875 m³   (b) 12 m²

Exercise 10F

1 (a) 700π cm³   (b) 192π cm³   (c) 1215π cm³
    (d) 625π cm³   (e) 576π cm³
2 (a) 1.46 cm (3 s.f.)   (b) 2.19 cm (3 s.f.)
    (c) 2.73 cm (3 s.f.)   (d) 1.24 cm (3 s.f.)
    (e) 2.19 cm (3 s.f.)
3 (a) Surface area = 1100 cm², volume = 2770 cm³
    (b) Surface area = 2010 cm², volume = 6910 cm³
    (c) Surface area = 9580 cm², volume = 23 600 cm³
    (d) Surface area = 149 cm², volume = 137 cm³
    (e) Surface area = 2540 cm², volume = 2510 cm³
    (f) Surface area = 252 000 cm², volume = 113 000 cm³
4 323.7 m³ (1 d.p.)
5 55.0 m² (3 s.f.)
6 Volume = 6760 cm³ (3 s.f.)
    surface area = 5590 cm² (3 s.f.)

Mixed exercise 10

1 (a) 60 cm²   (b) 21 cm²   (c) 27 cm²
2 (a) 30 cm²   (b) 6.3 m²   (c) 18 mm²
3 (a) 1.8 cm   (b) 2.4 cm   (c) 12 m
4 20 cm³
5 3000 litres
6 343 cm³
7 206 450 cm²
8 36 packets
9 For example, 28 cm × 15 cm × 24 cm
    or   28 cm × 20 cm × 18 cm
10 90 boxes
11 (a) 1080 cm³, 828 cm²
     (b) 2400 cm³, 1190 cm²
12 3257 cm³

Examination practice paper

Stage 1 (multiple choice)

1 E	**2** E	**3** A	**4** B	**5** C
6 C	**7** B	**8** E	**9** D	**10** A
11 E	**12** D	**13** A	**14** C	**15** B
16 E	**17** A	**18** A	**19** C	**20** B
21 A	**22** B	**23** C	**24** D	**25** E

Practice questions

Stage 1 (multiple choice)

1 C	**2** A	**3** B	**4** C	**5** D
6 C	**7** E	**8** D	**9** D	**10** E
11 C	**12** B	**13** B	**14** A	**15** C
16 D	**17** A	**18** E	**19** A	**20** D
21 B	**22** C	**23** D	**24** E	**25** D
26 C				

Examination practice paper

Stage 2 (Answers and markscheme)

Qu	Working	Answer	Mark	Notes
1	$150 \div 2.5$	$60\,\text{mph}$	2	2 marks for 60 1 mark for $150 \div 2.5$
2	$6 \times 3 \times 3$	$54\,\text{cm}^2$	2	2 marks for 54 1 mark for 3×3 or 9
3	$\begin{array}{r} 20.25 \\ -\;12.96 \\ \hline 7.29 \\ \hline \sqrt{7.29} \end{array}$	2.7	1	Correct answer only
4			3	3 marks for correct line 2 marks for 3 points correctly plotted 1 mark for line with gradient 2 or line passing through (0, 1)
5		4^4 5 1	1 1 1	1 mark for 4^4 or 256 1 mark for 5 1 mark for 1
6		e^9 $11x + 13$	1 2	1 mark for e^9 2 marks for $11x + 13$ 1 mark for $11x$ or 13
7		5×10^7	2	2 marks for 5×10^7 1 mark for 0.5×10^8
8	APB is an isosceles triangle $x = (180 - 40) \div 2$	$70°$	2	2 marks for 70 1 mark for recognising isosceles triangle or $(180 - 40) \div 2$
9		$(x + 6)(x - 6)$	2	2 marks for $(x + 6)(x - 6)$ 1 mark for attempt to factorise using 2 brackets and x and 6
10	$\begin{aligned} x &= 0.1272727 \\ 100x &= 12.7272727 \\ 99x &= 12.6 \\ 990x &= 126 \\ x &= \frac{126}{990} = \frac{7}{55} \end{aligned}$	$\frac{126}{990} = \frac{7}{55}$	2	2 marks for $\frac{126}{990}$ or $\frac{7}{55}$ 1 mark for writing recurring decimal as $0.12727\ldots$
11	$\dfrac{(x - 3)(x - 2)}{(x + 2)(x - 2)}$	$\dfrac{x - 3}{x + 2}$	2	2 marks for $\dfrac{x - 3}{x + 2}$ 1 mark for factorising top or bottom correctly
12	For C to be the centre of the circle it must lie on the diameter PQ. The angle between a tangent and a radius must be 90° so angle PQB must be 90°. In the diagram $CQB = 25° + 70° = 95°$ Therefore C cannot lie on PQ so C cannot be the centre of the circle.		1	1 mark for acceptable reason mentioning angle between tangent and a radius = 90° and why C cannot be the centre.